NATIVE INTELLIGENCE

NATIVE INTELLIGENCE

Raymond Sokolov

HARPER & ROW, PUBLISHERS
NEW YORK
EVANSTON
SAN FRANCISCO
LONDON

1817

This is a true story in the sense that it was entirely made up. Otherwise it bears no resemblance to real persons, living or dead, or to actual places or events, apart from certain historical tides and turnings already well known to newspaper readers and watchers of the nightly news on television.

NATIVE INTELLIGENCE. Copyright © 1975 by Raymond A. Sokolov, Jr. All rights reserved. Printed in the United States of America. No part of this book may be used or reproduced in any manner whatsoever without written permission except in the case of brief quotations embodied in critical articles and reviews. For information address Harper & Row, Publishers, Inc., 10 East 53rd Street, New York, N.Y. 10022. Published simultaneously in Canada by Fitzhenry & Whiteside Limited, Toronto.

Designed by Sidney Feinberg

Library of Congress Cataloging in Publication Data

Sokolov, Raymond A
   Native intelligence.
   I. Title.
PZ4.S6843Nat [PS3569.046]   813'.5'4   74–15893
ISBN 0–06–013910–2

75–76–77–78–79–10–9–8–7–6–5–4–3–2–1

For Margaret, Ada Jo, Tom, Josephine, Old Ray, Mike,
Joe and the other members of the Falcon Clan,
"whom monsters hold in awe"

Contents

Someone coming into a strange country will sometimes learn the language of the inhabitants from ostensive definitions that they give him; and he will often have to *guess* the meaning of these definitions; and will guess sometimes right, sometimes wrong.

—LUDWIG WITTGENSTEIN

"Queequeg, look here—you sabbee me, I sabbee you— this man sleepe you—you sabbee?"

"Me sabbee plenty"—grunted Queequeg.

—HERMAN MELVILLE

Foreword

This is the story of a few months in the life of a young genius who outsmarted himself. That may seem to be a callous way to talk about a good friend, but, to be perfectly honest with you, I think Alan Casper had it coming to him. He had no business being where he was or pretending to be who he wasn't. He knew too much about one thing and almost nothing about everything else. Really, I never liked him.

Then why did I write this book? The answer is that I didn't write it, not most of it anyway. I just collected bits and pieces of Alan's life—letters, diaries, documents. He scattered them everywhere and believe me it was no easy job tracking enough of them down to make a coherent story.

It's all true, as Balzac said, except that my lawyer made me change the names. You'll see why he did as you get into the book.

If you like it, you have no one to thank but me. Alan, obviously, was no help. His parents wanted to keep the whole thing quiet. The Peace Corps material is printed without official permission. The government of Qatab declared me *persona non grata*, and that faggot in the U.S. Embassy in Chiotteville tried to have me arrested for dealing dope.

I got what I needed anyway (not to mention a case of bilharziasis from swimming in Lake Qatab)—the facts behind a modern American tragedy, the intimate details of an unusual sex initiation and of an interracial romance, a close-up view of the impact of Western culture on the Third World, and, most of all, a new chapter in the history of the breakdown of language. Beat that.

WHY I WANT TO GO TO HARVARD*

Harvard attracts me for two reasons: Anatoly Martuszek and the prospect of finding the Golden Room.

I do not need to explain to you why Professor Martuszek's name rings with such magic. Anyone interested in linguistics is interested in him.

The Golden Room is a fantasy of my own. Perhaps I should not mention it, but I understand that this is a confidential document, and the Golden Room is the real reason why I feel impelled to abandon the reference room of the Flint Public Library, whose physical resources are perfectly adequate for my work in comparative morphology, for Cambridge.

I first had the vision of a place different from Flint at the age of seven. Having plunged into Dumas's *Memoirs of a Physician*, plunged, that is, without meaning to, into a world of intrigue, French names and fabulously intricate courtiers whose rhetoric glittered like a hall of mirrors, I felt suddenly at home. In such a world, I knew, I would fit; I would flourish.

In Flint, I fake it. I pretend I am not caught up in books and

---

*Submitted to the Admissions Committee, Harvard College, by Alan Casper, October, 1958.

grammar and music; I follow sports with as much enthusiasm as I can put on. I have some friends, but I don't take them seriously. They have read nothing and know nothing. The girls are the worst. At least the boys have some distant sense that they will be entering a career, will have to learn something. The girls I know look forward only to marriage and are preparing for that with little trial marriages—going steady—that are coy exercises in almost-sex.

I have tried that route and failed, not because I couldn't find a willing partner in petting, but because I had no stomach for the incredibly calculating process. Sex should be mutual passion, not a sly, protracted deal in which the man connives at getting his pleasure inchmeal and the women metes out favors grudgingly, like beads to a hostile Indian.

For ten years I have held to the hope that some day in another place I would walk through a door into a golden room filled with bright and glancing talk. No subject there would be too abstruse, no liaison too dangerous. Everyone would have read everything and thought the great thoughts. The Golden Room is the room whose existence libraries imply. It is the place to which Western culture leads us, men and women nourished by their civilization, sophisticated in life, experienced, witty and at home with their own lust.

The Room exists only in my daydreams. But in Cambridge, I hope to find something like it—friends who read Proust, women with the fiber to enjoy themselves.

[*The following comment was written in longhand below Casper's essay, evidently by a member of the Admissions staff.*]

Grades, SATs and high school recommendation all very high. We will, of course, accept him, but I think he is going to be disappointed with Harvard and depressed by Radcliffe. Another case of great expectations in the boondocks.

I

CAMBRIDGE

MASSACHUSETTS

MAY, 1963

May 1. *   May Day in other places, other times, meant something. The definitive thaw, the wedding night of the soil penetrated by the Maypole and danced upon by virgin youth; corn gods were appeased, plows sharpened and the world reborn.

Here May Day forecasts an end to fertility: reading period, exams and the fallow season of summer vacation. We commemorate the advent of bud and fruit only by pushing our heavy clothes to the back of the closet and by telling a story that should become the American myth of spring.

"Two couples spent their college years together inseparably. Then, after graduation and a double wedding in the university chapel, they moved to different cities a great distance apart. Occasional letters passed between them, but within two years even these stopped. Their only contact eventually came to this: on May 1 every year the couple in Baltimore would send a telegram to the couple in Seattle. It read: 'Hooray! Hooray! It's the First of May. Outdoor fucking begins today.'

"On the year of their tenth class reunion, however, the Seattle couple received no telegram. After waiting two days and

---

*Alan's diary has been drawn on selectively, by necessity, since many entries are purely technical and contain whole paragraphs in foreign alphabets.

checking with Western Union, they made direct inquiries through contacts in Baltimore.

"The Baltimore couple, they learned, had spent May Day on the roof of their renovated townhouse in a large Guatemalan hammock suspended between a chimney top and a wrought-iron guardrail. The aging chimney gave way, fell on them, and they were found, naked and still locked together, under a pile of rubble."

The cycle continues. My friends are spending the afternoon by the putrid Charles, grabbing each other in a bashful sort of fertility rite; grabbing hold, they hope, of elemental forces buried in themselves: a final caper in the sun before they make the switch from library desk to office desk, frustrated revelers threatened by a decrepit but still lethal civilization.

What am I doing? What would an objective observer, say a *Times* reporter, write about me today?

HARVARD SENIOR IN LINGUISTICS WINS TOP HONORS, STILL VIRGIN

Special to the New York Times

CAMBRIDGE, Mass., May 1— For the first time since 1937, Harvard will graduate a student with all A's. But the story behind the academic performance of Alan Casper, 21, of Flint, Michigan, is more than just a tale of 28 model bluebooks.

True, Casper, a gangly, six-foot-plus beanpole who could pass for the number one in a Jasper Johns painting, has just breezed through what is arguably the nation's most arduous academic obstacle course without upsetting a single hurdle. His thesis, "Semitic Origins of Greek Irregular Nouns," was a unanimous summa job that will be published by Harvard in the fall. And he is rumored to have learned 497 languages since his arrival in Harvard Square in 1959.

"That's if you count dialects," he explained.

But his friends around the Square, in this perhaps most elite of American college towns, say that Alan's grades are the least part of his legend.

Telugu and Malayalam

"Freshman year," said a former roommate, Abel Greenspan, "we used to kill time just watching him gobbling up the next language in the Widener Library main reading room. He did his formal course reading in the first two weeks of each semester and then switched back to his real work."

That year, reportedly, Casper loped through the grammars of such recondite tongues as Telugu, Malayalam, Siouan, Xhosa, Chuvash, Pushtu, Kachin, Mru, Yakut and Sara. Invariably dressed in black chinos and a buttoned-down white shirt with sleeves rolled up, he has become a fixture in Widener, paging through four books at once (a literary text in a new language, a grammar, an English translation and a bilingual dictionary).

The Maltese Flagon

"We used to try to trip him up," Greenspan recalled, "by asking him what the word was for flagon in Maltese or how to order a meal in rural Burma."

Once, Alan admitted to a weakness in Albanian, but he is said to have patched that up over weekends talking to waitresses at a local Albanian restaurant.

Indeed, much of his surprising skill in speaking foreign languages is due to extended conversations with native speakers in the Boston area: diplomats, immigrants and airline employees.

What makes Alan want to turn himself into a one-man Tower of Babel? A close friend who did not wish to be identified asserted that Casper "was a word junkie who raced after new languages because he was, underneath it all, a hysterical virgin terrified of women. 2,000 new words a week tend to take the edge off your libido."

For his part, Casper maintains that, professional reasons apart, he studies languages as an escape from the tedium of daily life, just as other people travel. Starting later this summer, he will escape even his own usual routine during a two-year stint with the Peace Corps.

That's about right. I am running away from women, but not because they frighten me. Like linguists, like everyone else I know, they want you to suck up to them; take them to dinner, buy them this, flatter them—all as part of a deal. A piecemeal transaction. With women you get a hand first, then lips, then the tip of the tongue, a breast. . . . That's as far as I've got. Stopped trying out of disgust at the process two years ago. Same thing with an academic career. You court them to get a Ph.D., then they pay you shit as an instructor. You write their kind of book, and they promote you up another tiny rung. By the end, when you've got tenure, you're so used to their mechanical, grubbing game that you can't do the work you originally wanted to do any more. That's why good scholars bottom out at 40. They've done all the deals they need to; there's nothing more to pimp for intellectually, and they've lost the urge to do research for its own sake. America is no place for smart people who won't whore to get ahead. Thank God I'm going away, even if it is as a knight-errant for Camelot. There are no golden rooms on this campus. It's time to look elsewhere.

May 5. I suppose I'm glad, on balance, that honors seniors don't have to take finals in June. It's nice being done and knowing I'm a summa. But that leaves a month with nothing to do. I can't seem to make myself read or do much of anything besides jerk off and solve British crossword puzzles. Came across a really difficult definition in a London *Times* in Widener today: "Plain things put a fish before the little county." Ten letters. Answer: "pikestaffs," "pike" plus the abbreviation for Staffordshire gives "pikestaffs" as in the "well-known" phrase, "plain as a pikestaff." Ridiculous.

Well, I have the linguistics colloquium to look forward to tonight. Even Herr Doktor Professor Helmut Blaupunkt of Magdeburg speaking on the comparative phonology of Micronesian labiovelars will be a relief after a day like this.

May 6. At first, it looked like every other weedy colloquium. Blaupunkt burbled away at the lectern, reeling off whole paragraphs of Micronesian poetry with a heavy German accent, realizing some revanchist dream of recapturing the Caroline Islands (on the linguistic plane this time, not the territorial, but the impulse is the same) for the Vaterland. Red-faced, belly pushing at the buttons of his quasi-tweed, unmistakably German jacket, he was trying to prove that Trukese and German must have some common ancestor because they have phonetically related personal pronouns.

Agronsky from MIT was leering with joy at the stupidity of the argument, waiting to pounce on Blaupunkt during the question period. The usual crowd of graduate students were there, too, putting in an appearance because they wanted to be seen and thought serious by whatever senior faculty happened to be present. Only old Krehbiel had bothered to show, which made it a wasted evening for the graduate students, since Krehbiel is retiring in June.

Parsons, a bearded 7G Sanskritist, had even begun to read the *New York Times*, noisily flipping pages by the time Blaupunkt droned to a guttural halt and called for questions. Agronsky immediately let loose with an irrelevant attack on Blaupunkt for not having used a computer-oriented approach to the problem. Blaupunkt shrugged. And then the most unbelievable thing happened.

A small and extremely pneumatic blonde seated next to Agronsky (I had assumed she had come with him) got up and said: "I would just like to call your attention to the pronouns in Burushaski. They are also phonetically similar to the pronouns in German and Trukese. Surely you don't suggest, Professor Blaupunkt, that there is some common language from which all three descend?"

Blaupunkt choked, as well he might. He hadn't taken Burushaski into account. No one ever did, of course, because no one knew it or had any good way of learning it, without traveling by jeep over crumbling Himalayan precipices to the Mir of Hunza. Burushaski is *the* linguistic anomaly, a totally isolated tongue, related to no other except for one dialect spoken in the same remote and almost legendary country. There was a grammar in print, but it was a notorious botch. And no one from Hunza had ever appeared on the outside to act as a native informant.

How, then, had this pug-nosed, lockjawed debutante learned Burushaski? More to the point, could she be persuaded to teach me a little?

I introduced myself and walked her into the Square. Her name is Missy Rand. She does premed at Radcliffe. As a child, she lived in Kashmir. Her father administered foreign aid in Srinagar.

"My ayah was from Hunza. She had learned enough hobson-jobson to get along with the other servants, but she was only really fluent in Burushaski. I picked it up from her quite easily. You know the way kids can pick up languages. Actually, I can still remember a lot."

We have a date for lunch tomorrow.

May 8

Dearest Alan,

Your father and I are counting the days until graduation. You are such a special son, and this is a special time for all of us. I do think it is unfair, though, that Harvard does not permit its valedictorian to speak at commencement. You would have something so important to say to your classmates, not to mention their parents.

Mary French talked my ear off yesterday about Jack getting into Western Reserve Medical School. I've trained myself not to brag back, just to smile inwardly. By the way, Marshall will be marrying little Sandy Stafford in August. We all wish you could be there instead of at Peace Corps training. Really, I can't believe they won't let you take the weekend off. With your record, they ought to realize you don't need as much time as the other volunteers. We can discuss this after we get to Cambridge, but—and I don't want to nag—please think again about writing the Peace Corps.

Love & Kisses,
Mommy

May 10.   I've tried everything I know, but Missy won't speak a word of Burushaski. "I don't want to be your informant," she says. "Once I'd taught you the subjunctive adverbs and the rest of the things you can't learn in a book, you'd drop me."

As it is, I'm hooked. We've spent practically every minute together since we met at the colloquium.

Greenspan saw us coming out of Albiani's today. Apparently, he knows her. Just a few minutes ago, he dropped over to congratulate me. He says she's a famous cold fish whom no one has ever got through to before. I told him what wasn't happening—no Burushaski *and* no sex—which inspired him to go through an hour or so of man-to-man advice about the art of seduction. The inch-by-inch theory that I hate. This once maybe I'll try it.

May 11.   Through the barber's window this morning, I saw
Missy walk by with Greenspan. They looked conspiratorial;
then they both laughed. I waved from the chair and caught
their eye. I must be wrong, but they did look guilty for a second.

Could this all be one of Greenspan's elaborate hoaxes? Is he
setting up Missy to seduce me? It's possible. If so, I may as well
play along.

June 10, 1963

Dear Sue,

Commencement is over. Alan drove off to Flint with his parents last night—in a station wagon packed solid with books. I am
sitting in my bare new summer school apartment over the Bick
feeling drained and very alone!

And so, at long last, here—to fill the empty hours!—is the
explanation I promised you.

I have been so happy.

Where to begin?

It started as a game. My part: seduce the gawky genius, destroy forever his fear of the vagina dentata and turn him on to
straight sex. And, oh, it worked! I played the demure virgin. He
had been coached by his friends to treat me as if I were shy as
a deer instead of the tart you've always known.

And so, while we waited to touch, we talked, and while we
talked, I fell in love. And then we made love—first in a cemetery and 22 more times in his room—and now he has driven
away with his parents to Flint, Michigan, where Alan will spend
two weeks before going to Peace Corps training in Louisiana.

I was his first; he was my fourteenth. I think, if he had asked,
I would have married him and got instantly pregnant to keep
him out of the draft. That's what the Peace Corps is for, a draft
dodge and also a graduate school dodge. As he explains it, if
you're a pacifist and an egalitarian, you can't fight for JFK or

take one of his student deferments while black kids get sent to
save democracy on the Rhine.

We had our month together, anyway, and he's promised to
write. I can hardly wait for the first letter, for obvious reasons,
but I also want to see if he can possibly write as well as he talks.

There we were, on our first date, at the Pamplona, with his
head grazing the roof and me running through my usual ten-
minute spiel on coming of age in Kashmir—the bright, white
colonial house with ten servants including a full-time tailor,
food covered with silver leaf, valleys of flowers, cool green light,
the rogue elephant that invaded our school—and then he
started to tell me about elephants, for an hour—elephant
zoology, elephant history, elephant anecdotes, the ivory trade,
tips on how to ride them, clever things to do with their shit, you
name it. He might have been majoring in elephants.

The next night, after seeing Renoir's "Le Crime de Monsieur
Lange," he switched to windows. He had this brilliant theory
about window imagery in the movie and windows in general,
what they meant to Northern Europe when they first came into popular use, brought light into houses, probably increased
the suicide rate, how Hitler forgot to expunge *Fenster* from
German along with the other non-Germanic loan words.

We were holding hands. He looked uncomfortable and kept
on about windows.

Before we finally managed to make it, he had covered wading
birds, the pineapple, gypsies and the history of Negroes at Harvard. Occasionally, he would ask me obliquely about Burushaski, the language I picked up in Kashmir. I would change the
subject; he would look wistful and start up again with a new
topic. Am I making him sound dull and didactic? He never was.
It seemed sometimes as though he had been planning our conversations for years and was desperately glad to have someone
who would play along, take him seriously.

One afternoon, during parietals, he asked me what I expected from sex—an appropriate question since he was just

then cupping my left breast—and, falling back into my stern-virgin role, I quipped: "Babies, and none today, thank you."

He didn't say anything for at least ten minutes, took his hand away and put on a record. I was sure I had blown it right then and there.

But he called me the next day. We went for a drive in someone's car, all the way to Provincetown, ate a linguica sandwich in a Portuguese place and walked on the beach.

"This will probably sound like some kind of line," he said. "And I guess it is. But I am really interested, puzzled and furious, in fact, over why anyone as smart and healthy as you should want to stay a virgin. Look, I don't want to be sexually pure. Why should you? There's no point in it."

Did I ever want to agree and say, "Let's do it then, Alan. Let's ball right here on the beach. Put your big long cock inside me where I've been wanting it for days."

But it was too late. I couldn't tell him the truth any more and admit I'd been fooling him the whole time. And so I went over and sat beside him on a dune and we kissed and he put his hand on my knee and then moved it slowly upward until he had it where we both wanted it. And then I remembered my period was still happening. So I stood up. And he didn't even look surprised. I knew he was telling himself: "This will take more time. She's as silly as the rest of them."

I could barely stand it. But what could I say? Driving back, it was dark and Alan recited from Browning's *Sordello.* I couldn't make sense of half of it, but I knew he was on the point of dumping me and couldn't think of anything civil to say.

The rest is history. I made an honest man of him two days later by the grave of a certain Letitia Forbes (1877–1879). My all but vanished menses made it into a kosher defloration. Alan was a miracle. Five times, Susan! And, naturally, he had memorized the Kama Sutra.

The next day I thought it was all over.

Alan finally found out the truth from Greenspan. I should have known Abie couldn't keep his mouth shut. He's always hoaxing people and then gloating at them afterward. Remember, I told you about the time he sent a letter to the *Crimson* about rabid squirrels in the Yard, on Health Services stationery. Classes were deserted for two days and one freshman shot out a window in University Hall with a .22 rifle, trying to hit a squirrel near his dorm. Greenspan nearly got thrown out of school, because he couldn't resist sending another letter to the *Crimson*, signing his own name this time, suggesting that they should be more careful about checking their facts.

Anyway, Alan met me at the lab, and all he said was: "Greenspan told me."

"I'm sorry," I said, feeling wretched. Then I noticed Alan was smiling.

"It's exactly what I would have done," he said. "Really, we did the same thing, played roles, lied to each other, quite brilliantly as a matter of fact; we did what we're supposed to do, but for the wrong reasons."

"What do you mean?"

"I mean," by now his smile was a beam, "that we pretended to be teenagers, which was a very adult thing to do. Now we don't have to pretend any more."

I wasn't sure what he was driving at, exactly. What he said next worried me, seemed a little sick. He wanted to know all about what I had done before, when, with whom, what I thought about it.

And, well, I told him. I owed him that at least. And so we sat there while the centrifuge hummed and bacteria multiplied, and I told Alan about everything, even us at Madeira. And then he led me silently out of the labs, past the rhinoceros statues and the law school and Mem Hall and across the Yard into Widener, up to the reading room, into the stacks, down the elevator to level D, where it is damp and nobody goes, and we made love on the floor of the section marked Sports and Games.

Orange dust from old bindings got all over my clothes, made me sneeze.

Will I see you this summer? I have a couch and a kitchen that came with one chipped beer mug and a garlic press. I need help getting through the days, more help than Chem. 20 can give.

Love,
Missy

II

EN ROUTE

June 12. Waiting is the worst thing in the world, especially waiting in Flint. This little city is like one big front porch with a view of a 24-hour traffic jam. One bookstore that really just sells cards. A newspaper without news. Flatness all around us. And the time drips by in a beige trickle. I should have heard from the Peace Corps by now, because training is supposed to start in July. Could they have lost my address or my file?

Obviously, they will find me eventually, but what country will they send me to? Argentina: Pampas, gauchos, a blind old Anglophile writing enigmatic cameos in the darkness with his mother in B.A., I think they call it B.A. "One Across: Fabric of city life in Argentina; you can make it yourself in reverse. Batik."

There are no British Sunday papers here, only American puzzles. I'd write my own, but who'd do them? Send to Missy? Never found out if she's interested. More scientific than literary.

Probably I should have stayed with her, gone to graduate school, married and settled down to a long and happy life teaching comp. ling. methods to freshmen.

No.

That would be better than the army, which I won't do under any circumstances. I will not willingly work to preserve American hegemony abroad, carry napalm to the savages to protect them from comsymps with the holy fire of capitalism.

Wonder if Fieser has shown his famous napalm film in Chem. 20. So proud of it. Required viewing for premeds. Shining example of U.S. know-how.

"Two Down: Brown cow's other half jumps over herself and follows Katy's initial step in a display of practical skill (hyphenated)."

"Know-how." Same mission for the Peace Corps. Bring the wogs up to our level. Turn them into consumers for Westinghouse products. Coopt. Into cooperation with us, U.S.

Not my idea. For me, it's a free trip to an exotic place, to a new culture; it will be a chance to live a new language instead of memorizing its vocabulary, to come down from my scholar's perch and dance barefoot in the sun. For a while. A two-year paid vacation, time to forget about America, to stop being American.

Must write Missy.

June 13.   No news from Washington or Cambridge. Certainly no news here.

June 14.   Mammaries Are Made of This: A Fable.

A young girl of 11 woke up one morning to discover that she had grown breasts. Her sheets were covered with blood. She cried until her mother came in and said she had become a woman. Then they both cried.

On her way to school that morning, a man leaned out of the cab of a Mack truck and said: "I'd like to put my face between those love jugs, beautiful."

At school, the girl blushed frequently over nothing. Then she noticed Billy Hornbuckle staring at her chest. She blushed again.

After class, Martin Furuncle brushed her with his elbow as they passed in the crowded hallway. And Arthur Braude put his hand right on her yellow Orlon crew-neck sweater right over the cup of her new bra and squeezed. It hurt. The girl said: "Cut it out."

This kind of thing kept on happening over and over again for the next four years. The girl took to carrying her schoolbooks in front of her as armor against men's eyes and hands. But she couldn't always be carrying books. Meanwhile the breasts got larger and more troublesome. She learned never to run so that they wouldn't jiggle. She wore a girdle so her also growing rear wouldn't jiggle. Jiggling caused trouble. But when there was trouble, which there frequently was, the girl always said: "Cut it out." And the boys always did.

Until December 16, 1958, when she went to a skating party at the Old Mill with Sylvan Bite (pronounced "beet"; he was of French extraction), who kissed her in the rink's equipment room, where they had gone "to warm up," and while he was doing that, thrumming his tongue against the portcullis of her braces, slid his slyly unmittened hand under her turtleneck and onto the leftmost mound.

The girl was about to say: "Cut it out," as she always had before; however, she was sick to death of saying it and more than curious what would happen if she didn't. Syl Bite was also curious. He had carried a "natural sheath" condom bulging in his wallet like a tumor for years already in case of such an emergency, but one had never come up so far and he wasn't sure what to do with it. He continued assailing the mound, stalling for time.

Eventually, the girl found herself lying on a hockey net in the dark. Young Bite was rubbing against her. This, she learned somewhat later on, was known as dry-humping. Even through the combined layers of Levi denim, girdle and panty, it felt good, sent an unexpected shiver through her. Just then, Sylvan groaned.

"Now," she thought, "I am really a woman. I hope I won't get pregnant."

Back at home, she washed her bra and stole downstairs so as not to wake her parents. On the top shelf in the den she located *Patterns of Sexual Behavior*, a book she had meant to read for some time. In short order, it taught her that she had been mistaken. She was not a woman yet. She had not undergone coitus.

Reading further, she learned that coitus between man and wife was the preferred form of lovemaking in contemporary America as well as 92 other societies including the Lepcha. Coitus ideally produced something called orgasm, which was explained in a series of graphs and sounded like fun. Orgasm could also be generated, the book said, through masturbation, but there was no specific explanation of how a girl went about that. It had something do with touching yourself.

The girl touched herself, down there where the hair had grown all kinky and slick. She rubbed . . . all over . . . snagged a hair with her thumbnail . . . ouch . . . it began to feel good . . . better . . . best. After a minute or two, she repeated the experiment to make sure that she had followed the graphs. She had.

The next afternoon, she invited her best friend Marcia to sleep over. When their hair was up in curlers and they were about to go to bed, the girl asked Marcia if she had had an orgasm ever. She hadn't, but in a few minutes she had. The two slept soundly. And from then on Marcia always avoided the girl in school.

The girl felt ashamed for several days, until she reflected that she had nothing to feel sorry for. Giving and receiving pleasure was not bad. Certainly she had the right to use her own body as she liked so long as she hurt no one else.

Syl Bite was the first beneficiary of this theory. Its effects on him were all good. His self-image improved. He had better stories to tell in the locker room after basketball practice. And he got a part-time job to pay for his condoms.

Many others followed him. The girl developed a reputation

around her town as an easy lay, and the other girls ostracized her. Men did not. Indeed, by becoming a woman she had drawn closer to men and almost completely away from other females. She spent all her spare time with men, and she even became, after a fashion, a masculine personality. That is, she absorbed certain male ways of doing things. She did what she wanted, decided how to get it, and got it.

Her freshman adviser in college said, after emerging from the shower during their first "appointment," that she was right to plan a course of study in science because she had a "visceral understanding of the law of cause and effect."

She had also learned a great deal, even, by that point, about power. Her breasts gave her power and, paradoxically, a man's assurance, as did her decision not to deny her own physical nature because other young women did.

But she was still a woman. And the men who were only too willing to join her in bed still thought of her as a woman, which meant that they construed her sexual zeal as submission to them. They soon came to see the truth, however, and disliked it. The girl had not submitted but joined in. The girl was her own man.

The girl, incidentally, was called Missy, and she continued to feel misunderstood and lonely, though she was never alone, until the end of her junior year, when she met . . . but that is another story.

June 19

Dear Alan,

I almost called you aldehyde. The labs last practically all day. I've got carbon rings in my dreams every night—as well as visions of a tall linguist on a white horse—and during the day, I lose track of what Fieser is saying, planning my trip to Zanzibar or wherever they'll send you.

Where *are* they sending you! It doesn't seem fair to keep you in the dark so long. Meanwhile, I can't see why you don't sit it out here with me. I just bought a dining table and curtains. I have plates and silverware. Yesterday, I even cooked dinner. My old Madeira roommate, Sue Flaste, is staying with me for a week. Greenspan dropped in, and I made spaghetti carbonara. He's hanging around Cambridge waiting for medical school to start. Can you imagine what will happen when they let him loose among the cadavers!

He wanted to know if I'd heard from you. It was embarrassing. Please write something.

Love,
Missy

PEACE CORPS WASHINGTON
806 Connecticut Avenue N.W.
Washington, D.C.

June 19, 1963

DEAR MR. CASPER:

Please be informed that your Peace Corps assignment is to the State of Kerala, India. You should report for training at the center in Honolulu, Hawaii, on June 28. An airplane ticket is enclosed as well as information on what to bring.

The Kerala project is still in the planning stages at this moment. No further details are now available.

Yours truly,
GEOFFREY SCHMIDT,
Supervisor for India

June 19

Dear Missy,

Thanks very much for the invitation. I would love to taste your spaghetti carbonara, but there's no time. The Peace Corps wants me in Honolulu for training by the 28th. The mystery is solved. They're sending me to India, to the state of Kerala,

which couldn't be better. It's coastal, Communist and speaks
Malayalam. What a mix: collectivized beach parties and a lan-
guage even I don't know very well. Maybe you can visit over
Christmas.

I'm off to the library to look for a Malayalam grammar. Write
me here. Mom will forward mail. Once I've reached the teem-
ing subcontinent, I'll send my address.

Regards to Greenspan and La Flaste.

Happy acetones,
Alan

STATEMENT FILED BY ALAN CASPER BEFORE JUDGE MILTON SOBIESKI, FLINT MUNICIPAL COURT, THIRD PART, FLINT, MICHIGAN, JUNE 20, 1963.

Yesterday, at approximately 11:30 A.M., I was in the reference
room of the Public Library, reading Finley's *Malayalam for
Christian Missionaries.* A friend of mine from high school, Sam
Klein, whom I had not seen for several years and who, I learned,
is now employed as an organizer for SNCC, the Student Nonvi-
olent Coordinating Committee, invited me to join him for
lunch. We left the library and walked to McNamara's Keyboard
Lounge, 143 Cherry Street, three blocks away. Outside
McNamara's, I met a colleague of his from SNCC, Miss Dinah
Dixon, of Tupelo, Mississippi. She and Mr. Klein had previously
arranged to meet there for lunch. The three of us went in to
McNamara's, which is very dark and decorated with automobile
hubcaps. We ordered beer. The waitress asked to see Miss Dixon's proof of age. Miss Dixon produced three pieces of identifi-
cation. The waitress took them and went back behind the bar,
where she appeared to be conferring with the bartender. She
then returned to our table and asked us to leave, saying that
Miss Dixon was obviously under-age and had given her a set of
false IDs. Mr. Klein said that Flint was worse than Mississippi,
because at least there, when they didn't want to serve a black

person in a bar, they said so straight out.

The waitress returned to the bar, spoke again to the bar-tender, and then began to dial a telephone call. It seemed obvious to me that she was calling the police. At about this time, three men who had been sitting at the bar came over to our table. They placed themselves around the table. One stood behind each of us and they started to make insulting remarks about Miss Dixon. After a few minutes of this, the man behind Mr. Klein spat in his hair. I told him to go away and leave us alone.

Just then, someone in the far corner of the room—it was too dark to see what he looked like—threw a glass sugar container and hit Mr. Klein with it in the back of the head. Mr. Klein slumped forward, unconscious. I reached forward to help him. The man behind me held me back and began choking me. The man behind Miss Dixon put his hands on her breasts. I broke free and a fight ensued. It lasted only a few seconds, because the police arrived and arrested me, Mr. Klein and Miss Dixon.

June 20.   So it has finally happened to me. After all these years of hearing about sit-ins and racism and police brutality, I've seen it all, close up, right in Flint. The brawl in the bar was bad enough, but the police were the worst, casebook sadists, clipping us with pistol butts all the way to the station, feeling up Dinah, stealing Sam's money.

Jail. A filthy lockup out of the movies. They threw us into a dormitory cell minus our shoelaces and belts. The first thing I noticed was a toilet in the corner with no cover. Rock and roll was piped in through a speaker on the wall that was too high to reach and impossible to turn off. Six men were already there, lying on cots. All black, young and coming down from heroin, coming down fast, in pain. One man wore a dress. His front teeth pointed in six directions. Untouched metal trays from lunch littered the floor. Green mutton and stacks of limp white bread.

No one talked, except for a big muscular adolescent who

mumbled "banana" over and over again. Dinner was at 4:30, Velveeta and more bread and hot water with flecks of chocolate floating in it. No one ate.

They wouldn't let us call anyone. I tried to sleep, but the night guard kept tossing lit firecrackers into the cell, ladyfingers. You had to stay up so they wouldn't go off right in your bed.

Next morning, the charges were dismissed; I'm free to serve my country.

PEACE CORPS WASHINGTON
806 Connecticut Avenue N.W.
Washington, D.C.

June 21, 1963

DEAR MR. CASPER:

Through a clerical error, you were incorrectly assigned to the Kerala project, which is already completely staffed. Please be advised that your name has been sent, where it should have been originally, to the Gabon project. Training will take place in St. Croix starting July 1. Please return your air ticket to Honolulu. You will find a new ticket for St. Croix enclosed in this letter.

Yours truly,
STEPHENSON HASTINGS,
Supervisor for West Africa

June 21

Dear Alan,

Kerala sounds terrific. I know you will like India, especially with your fluency in Burushaski. Me, I will pine and try to keep myself pure for you at Christmas. We can go to Hunza and see my nanny if she's still alive. Actually, she must be. They all live to be at least 135 there.

Enough small talk. I had better tell you what's been happening here. To begin with, Sue decided to stay with me all summer. She got a job at the Mandrake and hasn't tried to lay a hand on me yet.

Enter Greenspan. For some reason, he got interested in Sue, who is, of course, not in the market. And he started dropping in all the time, bringing very good grass. Marijuana has become very big in the Square this summer.

Anyway, for three or four days running last week, G. would come over and smoke with us. Nothing much happened. We giggled. Sue ate three boxes of Frosted Flakes, dry. Once, we took off all our clothes, but the grass made us so cold we put them back on and fell asleep watching the late movie with the sound off.

Meanwhile, I'm on another trip, a bad one, with Fieser. And I am very horny. I almost went to a Yard punch to pick someone up. How are things in the heartland? Things are not fine here in the Athens of America.

Love,
Missy

June 23.   No one can understand ennui, dullness, until he has spent three days sitting on a front porch in Flint. As far as the eye can see only sycamores and other front porches and well-cut lawns. An occasional delivery truck slices the empty serenity. Yet ten minutes away is one of the largest factories in the world, and in the other direction a dark bar and a musical jail with all-night firecrackers. Firecrackers. Sitting here on the front porch, America's unique contribution to the dictionary of architectural forms, firecrackers mean one thing only—the Fourth of July. We grow up on front porches and later learn that the quiet is noisily maintained in another part of town, on the wrong side of the tracks. White and black. Freedom and repression, wealth and poverty. The country is schizoid, always has been. Think of the frontier: fights in saloons and square dances, lynchings and temperance. The tension is still in all of us. Two generations of running the world haven't bred it out. Look at the Chevrolet workers, the guys who stand all day on the line tightening the same bolt with the same power wrench. How would anyone label them? Workers, of course, unskilled workers. And without pressing on Marx too hard, you would argue, if you didn't know better, that they would hate refinement, despise the people over them, want to topple them. Instead, they keep running that drill and buy their own front porches, smaller than the originals but they still have gliders. They couldn't favor property rights more strongly, and they love that feeling of safety a patch of lawn can give in America, safety from another side of ourselves that not only just learned which fork to use but still will beat the shit out of the next guy if he owns up that he really isn't a happy, middle-class, pleasure-deferring lawn mower whose true ambition is to re-establish the mood and standards of the McKinley administration. Lemonade on the front porch, and all is well. The natives are not restless, or at least we can't hear them because they are not living in this neighborhood, thank you, breeding and slashing and dancing and prancing and swinging their hips and definitely not running power drills or mowers. The darkies, as we conjure them up while sitting on the front porch, are a vision of the American pastoral, life running riot, not giving a rusty fuck about getting ahead, colonized but undominated. Infuriating.

Here I sit, a WASP out of sympathy with the order of the hive. What can I do about it? Sit in? Work for the government in Gabon teaching the American Way to yet more blacks? Fight for Uncle Sam? Stay in school and pretend languages don't imply social organization which implies politics? Get a job so that I can afford to surround myself with my own crabgrass?

If I had any talent or energy for political action, I would have to go underground, get off the porch and try to change things, like Klein. But I'm not political in the normal sense of the word;

so my choices are two. Either I can remove myself as much as possible from other people, plant nine bean rows at another Walden Pond, or, because the first alternative is a kind of suicide, because it is selfish and because it implicitly gives up on the future of the human race, I can spend time in another culture to see whether people uninfected with the American schizophrenia can cure someone who is.

Falling utterly into an un-American life, soaking in the language and, through it, the essence of another outlook, that will have to be my way out. Instead of altering my consciousness with drugs, I'll take the more interesting risk of exchanging an American head for a Gabonese.

PEACE CORPS WASHINGTON
806 Connecticut Avenue N.W.
Washington, D.C.

June 24, 1963

DEAR MR. CASPER:

This letter supersedes all previous instructions. The Gabon project was canceled yesterday by order of the President of Gabon. All volunteers currently on assignment have been given 48 hours to leave the country. As a result, trainees hitherto scheduled to participate in training for the Gabon project are being reassigned to other training sessions. You have been selected for the Qatab program.

The rigorous training for Qatab began yesterday in Ponce, Puerto Rico. Please proceed as quickly as possible to San Juan. You will be met at the airport if you notify me of your arrival time and flight number. A fare adjustment for the St. Croix ticket you now hold will be made in Ponce. I enclose a brief rundown on Qatab compiled by the U.S. Embassy in Chiotteville for the use of trainees. It is intended for internal government use only and should not be shared with members of the general public. That most especially includes Qatabian nationals.

Best wishes,

OVETA SINCLAIR,

Senior Officer (Qatab)

PERSPECTIVES ON QATAB

Introduction

Qatab, the poorest and least populated nation in Latin America, straddles the banks of the Mashmish and looks out over the Caribbean. Virtually unknown to the tourist, it exports 22 percent of the developed world's mahogany from its immense and still largely unexplored forest. Its 2 million people represent 11 distinct aboriginal, 3 African (ex-slave) and 3 European cultures (French, Spanish and Dutch). Since independence was declared in 1959, a modified form of parliamentary democracy has prevailed. French influence is still very strong, at least in Chiotteville (population: 175,000).

History

In 1495, Columbus dropped anchor in what is now the port of Chiotteville. His log reports that "three neatly made canoes paddled out to greet us from the green banks. They contained nine savages of slight stature, naked except for breechclouts and the red pigment which they apply to their entire bodies.

"We exchanged gifts, they giving us shrunken heads, we offering them hand mirrors, which pleased them as well as if they had been canaries. And indeed they immediately sang forth in a most musical gibberish. It would have pleased us to stay longer, but, descrying no settlement of any magnitude on shore, we contented ourselves with taking on water as well as several baskets of a most pleasant, elongated yellow fruit that grows in bunches of two score or so. The only drawback to the fruit, which the men have named banana because it resembles the nose of one of their number who is so surnamed, lies in its husk. It is easily peeled off and as easily discarded, only to cause painful accidents to those who slip over it unwittingly. . . ."

Spanish hegemony over Qatab began in earnest with the establishment of a permanent trading station on the estuary of the Mashmish, then known as Río Lóbrego, in 1546. The colony never enjoyed the prestige in royal Spanish eyes of gold-rich Peru. The local population was too small and too indolent for lumbering to be conducted on a grand scale. Indigenous hordes of carnivorous red ants and anacondas combined to make this the least popular outpost in the Hispanic Empire. And when malaria wiped out every Spaniard in 1708, no attempt to restaff the colony was made. Indeed, five years later, Madrid was only too happy to cede its grandiose territorial claims in the area to the Dutch through the Treaty of Utrecht.

The Dutch fared little better than the Spanish. Some of the mahogany log cabins built by the first settlers from Holland still survive, infested with termites and currently uninhabited. During the rainy season, descendants of the Balinese labor force imported in the 1790s use them for cockfights.

For over a century, the Dutch, perhaps wisely, treated Nieuw Nederland as an unseemly appendage to Surinam, which bordered it on the west. Native headhunters, who swept down from the Tumuc-Humac Range periodically, earned the colony an evil reputation. By the end of the Eighteenth Century, it was no more than a garrison of 200 Dutch dragoons, who gladly surrendered to an overzealous French naval party that sailed into Willemswijk (Chiotteville) harbor, all cannons blazing, midway through Napoleon's 100 Days.

Renamed Qatab (because Talleyrand confused the area with an unexplored portion of the Sahara), Nieuw Nederland was not stripped from France, like the other Napoleonic conquests, by the Congress of Vienna in 1815. Louis XVIII, with nothing

more than an old explorer's legend to support him, believed
that his own proconsuls would locate the city of El Dorado in
the fetid recesses of the Tumuc-Humac. The first governor,
Gaston Setouches, perished in the search, the earliest in a long
line of hapless explorers who entered the limitless rain forest
and did not emerge. His successor, Dieudonné Fourche, wisely
confined himself to the governor's mansion, ate no local food
(see below under "Diet"), subsisting on jerked beef and hard
tack shipped in from the Metropole, and slowly completed the
translation of Galen for which he still enjoys renown. His yel-
lowed, bulky, sweat-blotched manuscript is one of the main
attractions of the Musée National (see below under "Principal
Curiosities").

For 47 years, this shrinking scholar held on to job and life,
interfering seldom in the affairs of his colony or even in those
of his gubernatorial household. His motto was "Qui gouverne le
moins, gouverne le mieux." And it is certainly true that during
his tenure, no revolts, no atrocities and very little exploitation
of basic resources occurred. The mahogany industry continued
at its former pace, but smoothly, thanks to the efforts of several
thousand West African slaves imported in the twenties. The
French population stabilized at 15,000. Tropical disease killed
off roughly the same number of settlers each year, approximately 2,500, but annual immigration replenished these losses
almost exactly.

Fourche himself died in his sleep, and the modern era in
Qatab's history began. From 1867 until 1959, one ambitious
governor after another attempted to develop the colony. On
balance, their efforts now seem naïve, pyrrhic victories against
the jungle.

The Route Acajou, 150 miles of mahogany logs laid side by
side to make a bumpy thoroughfare through the forest between
Chiotteville and Morne Souriant in the interior, is now a mess
of dark splinters, seldom used despite the three stars it received
in the last Michelin guide published before independence.

The Lycée Fourche in Chiotteville, originally intended to produce an educated native class, still continues to service almost exclusively the children of French nationals and French ethnics. Blacks and métis (half-breeds), when they go to school, rarely continue beyond the age of 11.

During both World Wars, Qatab sent soldiers to Europe. Those dispatched in 1940 arrived in Le Havre after the fall of France, and spent four years at forced labor. Chiotteville flew the tricolor proudly throughout the Hitler years, offered refuge to the occasional partisan who found his way there, and was frequently mentioned as a bastion of freedom by General De Gaulle in his radio broadcasts from London.

From 1945 on, the ministry for overseas territories and possessions on the Rue Oudinot in Paris did its best to divest France of Qatab. But it took 14 years to create even a sham capacity for self-government on the banks of the Mashmish. Finally, François Tukuna appeared.

President Tukuna, a member of the Roucou tribe, was born in 1935 in the village of Klistor. Educated in the local missionary school, he learned as much as one can learn in six years of formal schooling in a jungle trading station. After completing the Roucou initiation rite, which gave his face the deep scars it still bears, he paddled downriver and worked as a busboy at the Hôtel de Chasse. Tukuna quickly improved his French and had risen to the position of headwaiter when, at the age of 20, he was recalled to Klistor to succeed his father as village chief.

In the joint council of the Roucou tribes, the tall and powerful young Tukuna flourished and quickly seized plenary power in the time-honored way. He killed the old pan-tribal chief and took possession of his wives and his flock of tame flamingos.

For three years, Tukuna ruled the Roucous from Klistor without once returning to the capital. He was virtually sovereign in his immense part of the forest. He lived happily on pounded manioc, deflowered a new virgin wife each spring and mediated between the various Roucou villages.

Then, on April 13, 1959, an emissary from the Rue Oudinot flew Tukuna by hydroplane to Chiotteville. It was assumed in Klistor that he was under arrest. And Tukuna was as surprised as any other Roucou when the last French governor kissed him on both furrowed cheeks and pronounced him President of Qatab.

There were elections, of course, but they, like all other technical aspects of his subsequent regime, were carefully managed by a skeleton crew of French advisers who stayed on in Chiotteville to maintain essential services—electricity, telephones and the Chiotteville branch of the Bank of France.

The same elections also established a Chamber of Deputies gerrymandered so as to assure the supremacy of the Roucous over other tribes. Since, in the bush, the Roucous had controlled only 20 percent of the country, if that, the official political disposition of Qatab, from independence on, has fomented deep division and a chronic state of guerrilla warfare. Only the lingering presence of 7,500 French soldiers enables Tukuna to hold Chiotteville. Large sectors of Qatab are now unofficially autonomous. Tukuna travels only among his faithful Roucous. His tax collectors have avoided most of the country west of the Mashmish since 1962.

Geography

Qatab covers 150,000 square miles. 135,000 square miles are jungle; the rest of the country is taken up by the Tumuc-Humac Mountains in the south. Aside from Chiotteville, there is no town of more than 1,000 in population. All rivers drain into the Mashmish. The climate is tropical. Annual rainfall averages 300 inches, all of which come between June and September. The temperature hovers around 85 F. all year.

Transportation

Chiotteville has 15 miles of paved road. There is a network of hard-packed earth tracks connecting the capital with nearby settlements, but these are impassable during the rainy season. Qatab's real roads are its rivers and streams. Powered craft are unable to navigate very far inland; the principal means of river transport are, therefore, the pirogue (dugout canoe) and the raft.

Since 1955, Air Qatab has maintained unscheduled service by hydroplane between the principal villages of the interior. QATURAN, the French-owned uranium company, operates cargo flights between its mines at Nouveau Biarritz and Le Lamentin, Martinique.

Population

The vast majority of Qatabians, 1.8 million by current estimates, live in small village units. 95 percent are illiterate and practice animism and geomancy. The eleven major tribal divisions have provided French anthropologists with a major area of study for 50 years. Space does not permit a thorough ethnographic survey. Most volunteers, however, will be in contact only with the three major tribes, the Roucou, who live within a 50-mile radius of the capital, the Ufa to the east, and the Xixi to the south.

In and around Chiotteville, there are a few hundred so-called Bush Negroes (noirs de brousse), former slaves who have returned to their original pattern of life in West Africa. Some are urbanized and Francophone; most are neither.

The capital, while mainly populated by Qatabians and métis who work in the sawmills, also has 10,000 residents of more or less pure European stock. Of these, 9,000 were born in Qatab. 500 are permanent immigrants. The rest comprise the transient staffs of various international enterprises and embassies. The American colony is exclusively diplomatic and numbers nine adults and two children. Last year's Peace Corps group started out with 20 members but lost six by attrition.

Languages

French and Roucou are the official languages. Counting major dialects, there are something like 27 other languages spoken in the country. Nearly every village has someone in it who speaks rudimentary French. Previous volunteers have not been successful in learning more than pidgin Roucou or Ufa. Xixi has proved even more difficult.

Diet and Health

Manioc is the only agricultural staple. Bananas grow wild. Small game abounds in all forms. The jaguar is prized but increasingly rare because of the safari industry. The rivers supply many kinds of fish. Some of the Xixi, however, will not eat fish for totemic reasons. Like the rest of Qatab, on the other hand, they consume flamingo and smoked cayman tail with relish.

Malaria, dengue fever, bilharziasis, yaws, leprosy, tuberculosis, Rickettsial pox, yellow fever and dysentery are endemic. The average life span is 27 years. Ten physicians minister to the entire population. Nine live in Chiotteville. The tenth is a WHO professional who crisscrosses the country by air. Qatab has no dentists, but tooth decay is not viewed as a problem of the first magnitude.

Latrines are unknown in the bush. Wells are often polluted by seepage or directly, since garbage and nightsoil are often deposited in wells, which provide a convenient dumping area, and no connection is seen between sewage and disease.

President Tukuna recently inaugurated a network of flush

toilets in Chiotteville, but it has remained inoperative since the first day. Official blame has been cast on the French engineers who installed the system. But privately everyone admits that the cause was local custom. Qatabians use leafy twigs instead of paper.

Currency

At the current official rate, 4.9 risps equal $1.00. There are 100 kalpans to the risp. Outside of Chiotteville, barter prevails.

Principal Curiosities

In Chiotteville, the Musée National (closed Wednesdays), 15 Rue de l'Horloge, has a rich but chaotically arranged collection of native crafts and mementos of the colonial era, including an exhibit of fouets de plantation, tapir hide whips knotted in fanciful patterns.

Tourists frequently take picnic excursions on the Route Acajou, which is passable on foot or by jeep for five miles from the city limits to a small Roucou shrine. Safaris by canoe can be arranged at the Hôtel de Chasse, 39 Boulevard Tukuna. The Ciné Plaza shows American westerns dubbed in French at 8 P.M., seven days a week.

Cockfights are the chief amusement of Qatab. No village is so poor that it does not boast at least one combat a week.

Independence Day

Treize Avril is celebrated in the capital and in all Roucou villages (other tribes protest their exclusion from the current regime by fasting and sometimes by disrupting the official celebration) with fireworks and barbecues featuring whole spitted tapirs. President Tukuna reviews a pirogue regatta from a stand on the east bank of the Mashmish outside Chiotteville. He and other government dignitaries smear their faces with red pigment and wear the traditional flamingo-feather headdress. Roucou dances follow the ceremony and continue through the night.

III

ENTER TO LEARN...

June 25. Thank me for flying American, Flight 209, Detroit-New York. Metropolitan Airport sweltering. Air conditioning "inoperative," they apologized, doubled our fun by departing two hours late. Meal count off so I miss dinner. Also miss connecting flights San Juan, by five minutes. Worst way. Ran through airport, wasted cab getting to Eastern terminal. Next flight at 1 A.M. Bargain fare. I save, or rather P.C. saves, $20. Eastern notifies "my contact" in Ponce.

Seven hours in terminal. Try every hour to call Missy. At midnight, a basso profundo, the legendary Sue, answers; seems flustered, says M. at the lab. At the lab? Yes, complicated experiment. Must be. I explain situation. Bon voyage, she says.

Bon goyave. Good guava. Fine tropical fruit, frequently made into jelly in Hispanic America and served with cream cheese for dessert. In Puerto Rico, they use some other cheese, forget the name.

Terminal fills with Puerto Rican families, native informants, a road company of *West Side Story*, taking it all back home. Lots of babies, chatter, Spanish without consonants. Does tropical climate make it hard to move jaw? Same in southern Spain.

Family next to me on long sort of couch, chrome and chartreuse vinyl, offer me drippy, juicy piece of fruit. Mango. Very good. They laugh when it gets on my chin. *Barba*.

Odd that beard and chin synonymous. Can understand confusion for men. But women? Linguistic machismo.

I am kidded about my formal Spanish—muy hidalgo—and we introduce ourselves. They are Julio Rodriguez, wife Isabelita, children: Julito, Juana, Felipe, Oracio and Dafne. Dafne blushes. She is 15 and very ripe. Others younger. Oracio just born and about to meet his grandmother.

Where am I from? Flint. Fleen? Means "pedernal," I explain. In Michigan. Do I have pictures of my family? asks Sra. R. Start to pull out wallet, but remember don't have any pictures. She assumes I'm an orphan. It's too difficult to explain that I'm not, that I don't need pictures of my parents, don't really need my parents, haven't since I was nine or so, when it came to me that we were all just living in the same house. In novels, would read about deep emotional ties between child and parents. Other language. Mother saw this too. Disappointed woman, but she insisted on going through motions all the same. Knitting sweaters. Baking cookies. Bragging to friends. Father gardened, kept to himself. Nothing to say to me. Embarrassed. Practically adopted Freddy next door.

Sra. R. gives me second mango slice, cutting deftly away from pit. Better in Puerto Rico, she says. Do I have a place to stay? A hotel? What is the Peace Corps?

An army to help people in other countries.

Who, she wants to know, will help me?

We get in line together. Boarding slow. I say something to Dafne. Another blush.

On the plane, I sit next to Sr. R. We have run out of topics and it is too chaotic to have to worry about awkward silences. Near the bathrooms, a crowd of teenagers has gathered. Someone plays bongos. They dance, sing. Babies squall.

It is still dark when we land. At the gate, I walk by a crewcut man in khakis and a blue Oxford shirt, buttoned collar, sleeves rolled up, carrying a small American flag. He taps me on the shoulder.

He is Bill Macomber, an instructor at Ponce. I look for the Rodriguezes but don't see them in the crowd. Macomber already has my bags in his jeep. They, it turns out, made my original flight. We drive off through San Juan into the countryside. It has just rained. The streets shine. It is 4:20 in the morning. No traffic. San Juan is a deserted movie set of plateresque façades, palm trees, Spain gone to seed, flashing neon invitations. A young woman in faded blue waves at us from in front of a bar open to the street. Macomber doesn't see her.

He is briefing me. I have already missed some crucial training sessions and will have some catching up to do. Qatab, he says, is no picnic. I have gathered that.

He stresses the importance of forming a cohesive group: "You'll really be glad to see a friendly American face after a month in some straw-hut village."

By now we have left the beach and are snaking along a pitted road into the hills.

Macomber drives very fast. The roadside is a dark green blur glimpsed through light fog. From time to time we bounce through a village of shacks with corrugated roofs. Macomber explains that "this squalor is nothing compared to what you'll see in Qatab, if you survive training. I suppose you've heard that the attrition rate here is 50 percent."

"What makes it so hard?" I ask.

"We do. Only a few people quit of their own accord once they're this far. The rest are fired either because they obviously won't last in the field or because they wouldn't do much for Uncle Sam."

"How can you be sure about things like that?"

"It's my business. I'm a psychologist and I did loyalty work for another government agency before this job. For instance, I can tell you're going to have a hard time. You don't show any enthusiasm about being here. Or about going to Qatab and meeting all the challenges there. I'm already worried about your ability to relate to other people. It apparently never occurred to you to thank me for meeting you in the middle of the night."

"Now, wait a minute. I haven't had much opportunity to build up much enthusiasm for this assignment. I only heard about it yesterday. The Peace Corps has been shipping me from continent to continent lately like a jute sack. And I certainly didn't think I was going to be given psychological screening at 5 A.M. by a perfect stranger who hasn't even bothered to welcome me after I stayed up all night to get here."

"You see what I mean. You're hostile and defensive. I try to help you out, let you know what goes on here, and you get mad at me."

I apologized to Macomber just as we pulled into the training center, which looks exactly like an army camp, which is what it was until two years ago. Now it's Peace Corps, Puerto Rico, or PCPR. That's pronounced "piss-poor," I found out from my new roommate, who is shaving as I finish this entry. His name is Ike Braun. He is short, just graduated from the Berkeley Law School and recently contracted a group of large boils on his ass. That is all I have been able to find out about him. Breakfast is in 10 minutes. 6:15!

June 25

Dear Alan,

I am furious at myself for not being home when you called last night. I wasn't at the lab. I was in Roxbury trying to find an abortionist. Now how's that for good news?

The University Health Services pronounced me pregnant yesterday afternoon. It must have happened that one day last month when I forgot to take my pill.

Anyway, Dr. Health Services practically threw me out of his office when I asked him if he knew where I could get rid of it. I decided against calling my parents. And so I started asking around the Square. Rico at the Unrest gave me a name. It took me half the night in a cab, in and out of black bars, to learn that Mrs. Broom has gone to the Vineyard for the month. Soft life.

By the time I finished looking for her, I was through with

under-the-table (on-the-table) abortions forever. Then, I crawled into the apartment feeling like Tess of the D'Urbervilles. (The cab fare was $45.) And Sue told me you'd called.

Puerto Rico, I thought, it's legal there. And Alan could be with me. It could turn out to be a terrific weekend. Don't you think?

I'm going to wait until after the hour exam in organic. So expect me on July 2. We can celebrate the Fourth together. They must give you that day off.

Don't worry about me. I feel fine now.

Love,
Missy

June 27

Dear Missy,

In a way, I was relieved to hear the news, because it meant that you had not been out with my new rival until the wee hours. I was very jealous. But now I think I have some bad news for you.

I have no idea where you got your information, but abortion was made illegal in Puerto Rico last year. Here is what you should do, immediately and without waiting for any hour exam. Call Eliot Parkman. He's a clubby I used to tutor in French so that he could pass the language requirement. He once told me the name of the Ionic Club abortionist. I can't remember who it was, only that Parkman assured me he was a well-trained, licensed doctor with rampant social ambition and no other way to satisfy it. Parkman must be spending the summer with his parents in Nantucket. Tell him I told you to call. On second thought, you might be able to get him to pay for the operation. He's so drunk all the time he never knows what he's been up to.

Seriously, if I could raise any money, I'd send it. Let me know anyway if you're short. And please write as soon as you can.

Training is tedious beyond imagining. We're learning a few

things, I suppose, but they would be better taught in Qatab. Mostly, we're under psychological observation. Nothing formal, you understand, but they're happy to let us know they're rating us all the time.

Love,
Alan

June 28.   Could it be that Missy really wants the baby? How else to explain that hopeless cab odyssey. Or, for that matter, the missed pill? I wonder when the last time she did that was. Still, she must be feeling horribly split between head and womb, and feeling, but not allowing herself even to think, that I should exit this patriotic farce, marry her and let her keep Alan, Jr.

It may come to that if I hear that idiot Creole instructor botch a few dozen more French subjunctives. Half the class is going to come out of this believing that r's are supposed to be converted into l's. Well, why not? At least, they're getting over their rooted, landlocked Yankee disbelief in the existence of foreign languages. Antoine speaks absurd French, but he doesn't speak anything else. For the first time in their lives, these kids are meeting someone who doesn't speak English. Up until now they could never latch onto a foreign language in school because, cut off by vast distances from any foreign countries except Canada and Mexico (the border and Mexico City don't really count as foreign countries), they couldn't help doubting that English wasn't spoken everywhere and acting unconsciously as if speaking French or German wasn't really like speaking Latin or, better yet, pig Latin, a word game that, if taken too seriously, would get you laughed at. Everyone really speaks American English when he gets up in the morning.

But Antoine couldn't possibly be pretending. He says what he says to converse with them, to say real things, not example sentences. He has no idea of how to teach—isn't supposed to have one; he's been hired just to talk with us until we figure out what he means—and so he teaches in the best way, the only way that works, by piling sentence on sentence, by forcing attention on words and sentences and idioms day after day through sheer force of character. He is worth understanding and so is understood.

Chomsky should come down here and watch Antoine too. The first class was enough to shake anyone's belief in the importance of deep structures. Antoine came into the room, all iridescent in his favorite green Tergal suit, carrying a stack of what looked like magazines. On top was a *Playboy* gatefold and underneath a couple dozen comic books. In one hour, he had taught the class five or six hundred words: all the parts of the body, the names of almost every object used in daily life plus the infinitives of the most common verbs. He would point to the appropriate picture, say the word and sometimes pantomime, while we repeated after him.

And now that we've gone on, inevitably, to sentences, Antoine keeps teaching vocabulary. He is barely aware of grammar in the usual sense and certainly would balk if you tried to convince him that language is a structure instead of a practically infinite skein of words.

He knows that, for instance, he is a better speaker of French than I am, even though I know the rules and he stumbles over them. I know you could argue that he's speaking his dialect and I'm speaking mine and that both are equally creative, equally transformational, give us infinite possibilities to weave new designs on our own warps, which are, in turn, strung on the same type of loom.

But that seems to me beside the point or certainly not a big part of it. What matters is what it feels like learning a new language or even operating with your native tongue. Everyone can master the grammar, just as any child can master the basic moves of all the chess pieces. We never finish, however, learning vocabulary, which takes constant amounts of rote memory work. New words are invented every day. New chess combinations are (almost) infinitely available.

Certainly Chomsky is right to attack the behaviorists, who think all speech is parroting. He does, however, overstress the importance of innate and concrete possibilities for structural creativity by individual speakers. Agree that the human brain is the ultimate source of coherent speech and of those celebrated sentences never before spoken, and you must still account for the way in which language is learned by everyone. And that is an endless process of imbibing vocabulary.

Take the case of Chomsky himself. He writes an article filled with complex analyses of the grammar of Dutch. Perhaps 200 people in the Netherlands will understand the article, even if it is translated. On the other hand, Chomsky does not know the Dutch word for "walrus," but it is almost impossible to locate a Dutch citizen who doesn't.

Who knows Dutch better? Chomsky or the guard at the Mauritshuis?

You will say that facility at linguistics should not be compared with facility at language. A linguist is, by definition, not a native speaker, but someone who explains native speakers to themselves. And yet the linguist who does not give native speakers a usable description of their practice is failing.

This objection should be applied to structuralism in general. Skeletons are not bodies. And, although it is fascinating to peel away the visible integument of things, we must not deride what we directly perceive as superficial or else we cut ourselves off from life.

Science indulges in value judgments about itself, despite every scientist's claim to a value-free enterprise. The judgments have to do with what is interesting, with what has heuristic value and thereby thrusts scientific discovery forward. The structure of DNA commands more interest today than the distinguishing marks of the bobolink. Molecular biology has all but supplanted taxonomy as a field of study. DNA is news; bobolinks are just birds.

But, you will say, isn't it finally more useful to press on into new areas, to make new discoveries that will, for instance, cure cancer or help us know more about the human brain? Yes, it is useful to do these things, to do science; nevertheless, it is not use *less* or less useful to keep established knowledge alive so long as it is still true. Ptolemy should not be the model for all previous learning. He was superseded, but Linnaeus was fundamentally not relegated to the junk heap by the passage of intellectual time.

There are two kinds of science then, descriptive and analytic. The analytic kind devours itself; the descriptive stops growing but does not die. Unless it is abandoned. In the special case of linguistics both types of science must inevitably interact. The syntactic pegboard means nothing without its lexical pegs.

But, you will say, the act of boiling down the potpourri of a natural language into a clear, convenient structure is intrinsically more interesting than the monotonous acquisition of new vocabulary, than, that is, the act of mastering the language as opposed to its rules. This is true. But the only way that linguists can make universally correct analytic statements about a language is to know the language. Indeed, ideally linguists should know all languages. This is impossible, but it is the proper goal. Das Wort ist alles, was der Fall ist.

June 29

Dear Alan,

Relax. You will not be receiving any Father's Day gifts for a while. It took almost 24 hours to get Parkman on the phone. He was still hung over when I finally reached him, but he hadn't forgotten Philip McGuire, M.D. It was embarrassing getting to the point with Eliot. Anyway, I did it.

Would you believe that your clubby friend offered to pay for the operation, which just happened to have cost $1,250, if I was willing to convalesce with him in 'Sconset?

Dr. McGuire fronts as a gynecologist in Needham. His office is all chrome and white formica and white tile, like a Mies barbershop. McGuire himself is about 35 and not bad-looking as blotchy redheads go. He has very big tufts of hair on his fingers; so I guess it's just as well he does what he does instead of dentistry. It would be safer for him, but can you imagine those hands getting caught in your bicuspids?

He had me come at 8 P.M., to the back door of the building, on foot. I got out of the cab a block away. Otherwise, except for the cash in my purse (withdrawn that morning from the Cambridge Trust where it has lain compounding itself quarterly since Grandmother gave it to me for college expenses, which, I guess, this was), it was very much like going to any other doctor's office. Better even. The nurse didn't pop gum and she showed me right in to McGuire's consultation room.

He asked me all kinds of questions. Part of them were medical. The rest were about Harvard, clubby Harvard: what game they play at the Porcellian (he said, "P.C." What an awful snob) and the name of the bartender at the Pudding.

The long and short of it was that I passed, and we went on to the next plateau. At Dr. McGuire's you pay in advance and you don't strip all the way. Just skirt and panties and shoes. In case they have to hustle you out in mid-hemorrhage, the job is easier. No general anesthetic either, which means it really hurt, but I could have walked to my car in case of trouble and arrived at a hospital without much evidence of foul play.

The rest was very quick and deft. McGuire was done in under a half-hour. He scraped and talked about his boat. Fortunately, I fainted after he'd begun a technical description of spinnaker strategy off Block Island.

I'm fine now. Just a little depressed. And how are you? If you don't write, I'll send Sargent Shriver my sworn affidavit about your sinister plot to spread godless Marxism all up and down Qatab.

Love,
Missy

July 3

Dear Missy,

I'm sorry you had to go through that expensive torture. Dr. McGuire sounds repulsive. Are you sure you're all right now? You may have lost quite a bit of blood. Shouldn't you see a straight doctor now?

I'm becoming a two-bit medical expert at the moment as part of the training, which makes me hyperconscious of the possibilities for physical breakdown. From what they tell us, it is almost impossible to stay healthy in Qatab. Everyone who stays more than a few days gets something. We're already taking malaria pills. They, by the way, make you temporarily sterile; so I will be a model companion if you can manage to come down here before we're shipped south on August 5. I can get a couple of days off any time.

The routine is pernicious. The actual training takes a lot of time, but isn't hard. A little French, a little hygiene, a little woodcraft. In the afternoons, we work at the Center. The work is supposed to apply to our future assignments. But I don't imagine what I'm doing on a road gang here will help much. We have a big vegetable garden, but climatic conditions are quite different in the jungle. Last week we dug a well with purposely crude tools, to simulate local conditions. The trouble there is that Qatab has hundreds of beautifully clear rivers.

They aren't telling us what we'll really be doing once we get there. Teaching English in Chiotteville is an obvious possibility. Health education is another. The actual job doesn't matter to me very much. I do care, though, about where I'll be living, with whom.

The training program avoids any instruction in local languages. Most of my fellow volunteers are having enough trouble with French, which they have studied, sort of, before. They probably don't have a shot at fluency in something exotic and non-Indo-European like Roucou, the official language.

I'm hoping they send me to a remote village that speaks

something never even written down before. I could put together a dictionary on the side and do field work for a Ph.D. thesis. And that kind of location would put me out of reach, too far away for the Peace Corps to meddle with. I can see already that they love to meddle.

A typical day here ends with a session of what the Stalinists used to call self-criticism. All 25 of us get together in the dining room over coffee and confess to our sins. Macomber, who is definitely CIA, sits in a corner listening. He's the staff member who met me at the airport and decided I wasn't gung ho enough.

To give you an idea of how these meetings work, I'll try to reconstruct some of what went on last night. The topic we settled on was selfishness.

Now you must know and understand, O Best Beloved, that each of us is constantly aware of being judged by Macomber, who has pretty much said that his reports count more than anything else in the decision whether to deselect us. Two volunteers have already been sent home. They were sleeping together, and that wouldn't look good in Chiotteville, they were told. But more important, according to Macomber—he expounds Peace Corps dogma on request—was the harm their "exclusive relationship" did to the group's cohesion. That's what brought up selfishness.

The session began with my roommate, Ike Braun. He is extremely cynical about confession sessions and takes great delight in inventing harmless failings. Last night, he revealed that he "occasionally" masturbates. I happen to know that he masturbates at least once a day. I can hear him at night. And I also know that he is sure the Peace Corps will smile at his peccadillo and like him for his sincerity and for his expression of guilt.

"I hope this won't shock any of you," he said, "but I occasionally masturbate. I am trying not to. I know it isolates me from the group emotionally and reduces my efficiency in the work program, but I sometimes can't get to sleep without . . . er . . . having an orgasm."

"I have read," said Alice Martin, a very earnest thirtyish schoolteacher from Topeka, "that nearly all young men your age do what you do every once in a while. I don't see anything abnormal in it. You seem to fit in real well with the group. I have a worse problem. I hate sharing a room. Nothing against you, Mitzi [her roommate]. It would be the same no matter who was lying there. I'm too used to having privacy, I guess. I don't know what I'll do if I have to live with a family in one room."

"Especially if one of them 'masturbated occasionally,' " said Jock Kramer, a very talented geologist who can't keep his mouth shut and will probably be deselected as a result.

"I wouldn't mind that so much," said Alice. "It's everybody looking at me I would hate."

"But they're going to look at you," I broke in, "all day long. That's part of what we're going for. To be looked at. To show them what we're like. Give them an example of American behavior up close. And you'll be looking at them, figuring them out."

"What about you, Casper?" asked Kramer. "What have you been doing against the group lately?"

"I've been thinking my own thoughts and putting them in a diary."

"What thoughts?" someone wanted to know. I wouldn't tell, which made them all nervous. I'm also sure I lost some points with Macomber on that one.

The sessions are all like that. Pretty dull, but they work. They break down private walls between us. They intimidate us into giving up the appearance of individual identities. Next, we start losing our real individuality. The process is already shaking up the only married couple in the group, Sarah and Bob Ashton. They feel under terrific pressure not to spend time away from the group. She told me last night that they hadn't slept together for days, because they're so busy mixing—playing bridge or going for hikes with the rest of us—that they never seem to go to bed at the same time.

Maybe it wasn't such a good marriage to start with. He failed at selling insurance for Prudential and picked the Peace Corps as a haven to think things over in for two years. He's stooped and slack at 27. A fish washed up by the tide.

She is a big, lean, earthy woman, the only person here without a college degree and very self-conscious about it. They met in a lunch counter in Indianapolis. He was on his way out of state after flunking orals in musicology at IU. She was a waitress looking for something better to do in a better town. He took her to Boston in 1961, and she discovered culture, or what she thinks is culture.

Sarah is an odd mixture now of half-digested reading and half-repressed gaucheness, a farm girl who's trying to fit in at meetings of the Browning Society.

No, that's not right. Browning is too old-fashioned for her. She affects the modern poets. You can guess which ones: Housman at his ripest, the polite Yeats. That's Sarah at the top of her form. For relaxation, she has a trunk of recent best-selling novels. Her current heroine seems to be Désirée, which is about right, since Sarah's body is the central feature of her dilemma. It is a big, healthy body, I must say, hard to ignore, harder for her to forget. She's a natural flirt, must have had a lot of men before Bob, and I doubt he's going to hold on to her much longer. Don't worry about me, though. I could never make it with a woman who says: "Between you and I, Edwin Arlington Robinson gives me a hard-on."

I miss you, and I am keeping you a secret as long as possible from the group. Come soon.

Love,
Alan

July 4

(*The curtain opens on a section of a park in Ponce, P.R. In the B.G. is a line of palm trees. It is Independence Day. Fireworks go off from time to time. O.S. a crowd shouts in response, mostly Spanish cheers but also scattered cries for Puerto Rican inde-*

pendence. Two young continental Americans enter S.R. She is tall with prominent buttocks and flaring chest. He is taller and remarkably thin.)

SHE *(out of breath):* We made it.

HE *(also panting):* Do you think they noticed?

SHE: No. They were too busy watching the natives. Getting into the culture. I'm so sick of being a hot-shit volunteer. You must be too or you wouldn't have known what I meant when I nudged you. I knew you would. I've been watching you, Alan. You don't like being part of the group. You're a bad volunteer.

HE *(smiling):* So are you, Sarah.

SHE: You're not kidding. I've tried, but I can't do it. Like everything Bob gets me into, I feel bottled up, like my balls were in a vice.

HE: Why don't we sit over there. *(He points to a bench. They sit on it. At this point, the crowd roars. He can't hear what She is saying. She leans forward to shout in his ear. Then She kisses him. They embrace.)*

SHE *(during a lull):* "The Lord has filled her chalice to the brim."

CURTAIN FALLS

July 10

To: Mrs. Sinclair
From: William Macomber
Subject: Alan Casper

This is an extremely smart young man but no team player. No difficulty is experienced by him in satisfying the requirements of the classwork. But he gives the impression of disdaining, or, I should say, of not getting very excited over, Peace Corps activities. It would not be fair of me to recommend deselection at this moment, nor do I think I shall ultimately do so, because his brain is important to us.

In most assignments, Casper would find relating to the locals in a way fruitful to us to be impossible. But, in my opinion, he is a good bet for the Xixis. He would be alone out there, and he would be seen by no one of official importance for months at a time. Every other personality profile has failed to move that tribe one inch out of the Stone Age. Maybe Casper can teach them to get off their behinds and lead productive lives.

His affair with a married female Volunteer (see memo on S. Ashton) in this training group will also not continue to raise problems once he is stashed in a Xixi village. They are being very discreet here, and communication on a regular basis will be virtually impossible in Q.

Finally, it would be awkward to deselect anyone else from this group. We are down to the bare minimum necessary to maintain an effective presence in Q. for the next two years, and it is much too late to find better replacements.

It is recommended that a copy of this be forwarded to Livingston Kaufman in Chiotteville.

W.M.

July 12

(The curtain opens on an almost entirely blacked-out stage. Moonlight shines through the small rear window of a tent. He and She are barely discernible lying on two cots pushed together.)

SHE: ". . . peace comes dropping slow, dropping from the veils of morning to where the cricket sings; there midnight's all a glimmer, and noon a purple glow, and evening full of the limpet's wings."

HE: Linnet's.

SHE: What?

HE: Linnet's not limpet's.

SHE: You're always such a martingale, darling. What difference does it make? It's the feeling that counts. You really made me feel, you know, three times.

HE: Six.

SHE: I know. I just didn't want to give you the satisfaction. You're so cocksure, such a change from droopy old Bob.

HE: Let's not talk about him.

SHE: We're going to have to tell him some time.

HE: Be serious. You and I share a common interest in nothing but sex. That's it.

SHE: What do you mean by that?

HE: I mean that it's preposterous for you to make this into more than it is. For Christ's sake, we aren't even probably going to be in the same place in a few days.

SHE: If we were married, they would assign us together.

HE: Oh, no! Hasn't one marriage been enough for you, Sarah? Stop fooling yourself. You're not built for monogamy. You need lots of men.

SHE: "The power is yours, but not the sight; you see not upon what you tread. . . ."

HE: Did you forget the next stanza? "Are you never to have eyes to see the world for what it is?"

SHE *(lunging playfully at Him across the cots):* You smart-acre. You know too much for your own good.

HE *(lunging back):* If I'm a smart-acre, you're a wise-aleck.

CURTAIN

July 14

Dearest Alan,

Did you get the salt pills I sent? Please don't forget to take them on hot days, especially after any major physical exertion. You're in the tropics, remember. Don't mind my saying so— I'm sure you are doing your best as usual—but this training period is no time to mistreat your body and hamper your performance.

You diploma came back from the framer today. I've hung it in the den with all the pictures of you. Don't worry, though, if you need it for your office in Qatab, I'll be happy to ship it down to you. I have already packed your ties—you seem to have forgotten almost all of them—and will send them as soon as you have a permanent address. Or should I mail them to the embassy so they'll be there when you arrive?

Nothing much is happening here, but we did get a visit from a Mr. Cassidy of the FBI. Don't be alarmed. It was a routine clearance check. They interview all the parents and close friends of volunteers in training. The questions were mostly quite easy to answer. He did want to know about the sit-in, of course. I assured him you had just been an innocent bystander. I hope you'll take a lesson from this and spend your spare time in Qatab with the other volunteers. Try to stay out of the Negro neighborhoods after dark.

Cassidy also wanted to know if you had had any experiences with girls. I was sure he meant you know what; so I felt truthful in telling him I knew the Peace Corps had nothing in the world to worry about on that score. You had always been too serious about your work—and too levelheaded—to get in trouble with women. Sometimes, I told him, your father and I had wished you had gone out on a few dates. You'll have to get married some day. Maybe you'll meet someone at training.

Everyone asks after you. Good luck.

Love,
Mommy

JFK VISITS PUERTO RICO

SAN JUAN, P.R., July 15 (AP)— President and Mrs. Kennedy spent a quiet two days on this sunny American outpost in the Caribbean. They swam and snorkeled in a private cove out of news camera range for most of the period but ventured forth, in yachting clothes, for a semiofficial tour of major government facilities on Sunday afternoon.

The President himself drove Mrs. Kennedy and a Secret Serviceman in an open jeep from the Governor's mansion to the Peace Corps Training Center outside Ponce.

After a bumpy but otherwise uneventful drive—local autonomists had planned a demonstration but were unable to find the presidential entourage before it had sped inside the Peace Corps compound—the Kennedys walked through the Training Center grounds and sat in on a French class.

Mrs. Kennedy joined in the conversation with her Sorbonne French. After class, the President congratulated the Volunteers on their work and their aims. Then, unexpectedly, he seemed to recognize one of the young people, moved forward as if to shake his hand, stopped short, blushed and departed. Neither the youth nor the President's press staff would offer any explanation for the incident. A Navy helicopter flew the Kennedys back to Air Force One.

July 15. He must have remembered me. That's clear. I wonder if that means I'll be deselected.

It's a fact that I remember seeing him. He had come from Washington for an Overseers' meeting. Harvard was in full preen: the President is also an Overseer, one could say to oneself and feel all the more certain that Cambridge was the true center of the nation.

Late that afternoon I was walking by the Bick and happened to look in. There he was, sitting over coffee and English with a very trim woman in her thirties. That was enough to make a good story. But I also happened to notice that they were holding hands under the table. He pulled his hand away as soon as he saw me. I must have really been gawking at them. But after all . . .

Macomber is suddenly very interested in me—and wary at the same time. What do I know? Am I dangerous to him? Should he squash me or cultivate me? He is more disgusting than I first thought. I'd certainly like to see his mail tomorrow, though.

DOS187 PROMACOMBER PONCE EXUNDERLORD
HANDLE TALLBOY WITH UTMOST CARE. HIGHEST ECHELONS MOST INTERESTED HE NOT INTERPRET ANY OFFICIAL ACTION AS BIASED AGAINST HIM. THIS OFFICE ADDS ITS ENDORSEMENT ALTHOUGH NO EXPLANATION FOR ANY OF THIS CURRENTLY AVAILABLE. ASSUME YOU IN POSSESSION OF RELEVANT FACTS ALREADY AND WOULD HIGHLY APPRECIATE FILL-IN. ALL FURTHER COMMUNICA-TIONS MUST BE IN SYNTAG CODE NUMBER 9Q*H RPT 9Q*H.
THANKS & REGARDS

July 16. Something is definitely up. Macomber called me in for a meeting today. First, he tried to get me to talk about JFK. I said that it was nice he took such an interest in the Peace Corps. Then Macomber asked me what I thought of training. Poker-faced, I said I was finding it a challenge but also a wonderful opportunity to learn to work with other people. I was sure it was excellent preparation for the field.

He nodded, got up from his desk and went to the filing cabinet. Out came a fifth of Chivas. He poured two very tall mahogany tumblerfuls of neat Scotch and handed me one.

"Alan," he said, sitting down on a captain's sling chair next to me, "I'm sure you also have some criticisms of what you've been through. A young man as intelligent as you are must have seen ways in which this program can be improved."

I tried a little of his Scotch and offered: "People at your level should be issued refrigerators."

"No, I'm very serious. The Peace Corps wants to do a better job. I can assure you that any idea you propose will be taken very seriously."

"Well," I began, figuring this was some elaborate plot to draw me out and then use whatever I said against me, "I think Antoine should be better paid. He doesn't complain, but it's obvious that he needs more money; and he deserves it. He's a wonderful teacher."

"Excellent. Anything else?"

"It would be a relief if there were occasionally a movie to see. Bridge, charades and self-criticism get dull after a few weeks."

"What would you like to see?"

"Oh, it doesn't matter that much."

"No, really. Give me a list. I'll see what we can do."

So I did. I gave him a list of movies that are usually impossible to see because they've been retired by their distributors: *Stagecoach*, Pagnol's trilogy, the lost and legendary uncut version of *Greed*, *The River* (Jean Renoir's virtually unobtainable classic set in India). I also suggested, as part of the language program, that we should view current French movies with the original track and no subtitles. Macomber nodded as if I had asked for the simplest things in the world.

We then proceeded to get roaring drunk together and he told me the filthiest joke I've ever heard, a story about newlyweds and chewing gum. A strange guy. I wonder if JFK was behind his sudden chumminess. Anyway, I don't see how I could have got in trouble saying what I did.

July 18. Incredible.

Antoine came to class today in a new, seersucker suit and wearing a Swiss watch. We spent the hour talking about the virtues of the American Way of Life and how it rewards hard work.

Out the window, I noticed an army truck unloading a huge crate and a couple of small ones. A brigadier general supervised the unloading. The big crate held a 35-millimeter projector. It took all day to rewire the dining room for it.

After lunch, a film schedule was posted on the main bulletin board. The list was very familiar. Tonight we see *Stagecoach.*

All of tomorrow is being devoted to a nonstop screening of *Greed*. On Friday, we get *A Bout de Souffle*. It must be a French print or they would be calling it *Breathless*.

I guess I should have asked for more. Maybe it's not too late. Better not push my luck too far, though.

July 17

Dear Alan,

So the First Family dropped in on your humble French class. Could that possibly have been you who made JFK stop in his tracks? You never told me you were part of the presidential past. Promise you will tell *all* on the 26th.

I'm landing at 1:22 P.M., Pan Am 336 and booked into the Miramar for two nights. Will that work out for you? I'll rent a car at the airport. Write immediately if you want me to switch something.

What can I bring you from North America?

Love,
Missy

July 19.   Macomber didn't know what to think when I asked him for permission to spend the weekend away from the Center. On the one hand, he was pleased to be able to grant me an easy favor. On the other hand, he was suspicious; I could see his spook instincts reacting: what kind of mischief is this kid up to now, planning some secret phone call or what?

I told him the truth, which means he is going to tail us all weekend. This has got to stop. I think I know how.

July 19

My dear Mr. President:

I am the Peace Corps Volunteer you thought you recognized a few days ago at the Ponce Center. Although I would be proud to claim your acquaintance, I cannot. Nor to my knowledge have I ever seen you except at this Center. I do not know whom

I reminded you of, but I think your memory must have played a trick on you.

It may amuse you to know that your mistake has brought me some local notoriety, to which I am not at all entitled. I am *sure* that will die down very soon, but it has been great fun while it lasted—a pleasant brush with the power of the presidency but also an unpleasant reminder that the limelight is very bright. Why, if some schoolchild in Ponce were to see me do something as tame as hold hands with a girl, it would be all over the island in minutes. Now I really understand why famous people yearn to be left alone and *forgotten.*

I know you will forget me almost *immediately.* I, on the other hand, will never forget you.

Very truly yours,
Alan Casper

July 20.   I hope that letter gets through. Macomber or some-body has been going through my things. Luckily, I was writing in this on the mess hall steps. Now I'm going to have to lock it up. Should have been doing that anyway.

Do you suppose Macomber has bugged this place? And Sa-rah's? He won't have much to listen to from either recorder, especially the one under her floorboards. God she has a big ass, like two lumps of lard, and mottled.

Why am I bothering with her?

1. She is a tiger in bed.
2. It is not worth the trouble of breaking off. We'll be sepa-rated in a month anyway.

IN A MONTH. That's it. Belmondo was quoting from *Bérénice.* It has to be.

He and Seberg are sitting in her room, and she won't go to bed with him. He asks her, "Then when will you? In a month? In a year?"

"Dans un mois, dans un an? . . ." Godard must have meant the allusion. That phrase is almost as famous as "To be or not to be . . ." Every French schoolboy knows the speech. But why should Godard put a fragment of it into *A Bout de Souffle?*

Because it fits perfectly with what he is setting up about language, and by extension modern life, in the film. Both Belmondo and Seberg speak corrupt French. She is an American drifter forever asking the meaning of French words, using a laughably bad accent. He is a foul-mouthed gangster ("If you don't like Nature, go fuck yourself") who speaks dialect and argot. He counts by the Swiss system, says "septante" and "huitante" for "soixante-dix" and "quatre-vingt." His alias (Laszlo Kovacs) is ostensibly Hungarian but actually lifted from an American cinematographer.

And there they sit in her tacky room, two kinds of neo-riffraff, desecrating French, aspiring to no standards of nobility in conduct, utterly ignoble, morally nerveless, committed to each other by the dingiest, most listless and minor sort of impulse. This is no romance. The two of them barely can muster the appetite even for sex. Major passion is not their line.

And yet a morsel of that purple passage from Racine dribbles unnoticed from his mouth. The irony is tremendous. Think of the speech:

> Dans un mois, dans un an, comment souffrirons-nous,
> Seigneur, que tant de mers me séparent de vous;
> Que le jour recommence, et que le jour finisse,
> Sans que jamais Titus puisse voir Bérénice,
> Sans que, de tout le jour, je puisse voir Titus?
> Mais quelle est mon erreur, et que de soins perdus!
> L'ingrat, de mon départ consolé par avance,
> Daignera-t-il compter les jours de mon absence?
> Ces jours si longs pour moi lui sembleront trop courts.

Godard wants to make the viewer think for a flash about this pinnacle of classical, Latinate rhetoric, of French as it is taught, of distant times and noble passion that shook a king and queen, of a renunciation that was beautiful and beautifully expressed. The reference is quick, it jumps by like one of Godard's revolutionary cuts, and jars the mind.

From the messy bedroom of the neo-tart, who can give no reason and summon up no ardor for anything she does, who can barely speak to her lover, who betrays him indecently, who watches his death without a twinge, whose command of French is too slight to understand Belmondo's final croak: "C'est dégueulasse," we are transported by the subtlest kind of literary allusion, an apparently colorless phrase culled from a famous passage, to the lofty, Alexandrine declarations of Titus and Bérénice. Godard compresses this irony into a brief moment, sets off the highest of French styles against the lowest, and deftly places his characters, by implication, at the bottom end of a moral scale running from the degraded to the sublime.

You will say that I lay too much emphasis on a perfectly normal French phrase, that Godard may have intended nothing by the line. Consider the following: in an American movie, an indecisive young male character trying to decide whether to do something or not poses the alternatives to himself and then says, "That is the question." Do we have an allusion or don't we?

Moreover, Godard's special interest in the big speech from *Bérénice* is explicitly shown in a scene in *Une Femme Mariée.* The heroine and her lover are in bed together. They read the actual lines of the relevant scene from Racine just prior to his departure for Avignon, where he will play Titus on the stage. Ostensibly, she is helping him learn his part. But obviously this modern and adulterous couple sneaking time together in an airport motel are meant to be seen as shabby descendants of Titus and Bérénice. They, too, will separate physically, but they are making no sacrifice of any consequence. Also, he gets his lines wrong, and has to be coached to speak nobly.

And where does all this leave me and Sarah?

We're not much better than Seberg and Belmondo. Maybe we're worse. We barely speak at all. It would mean nothing if we never saw each other again. Or does it count for something to have committed our bodies totally to each other for a few days? Clearly, Sarah thinks so. She thinks she is in love with me. Does she imagine that I will ever want to live with her?

Picture that. She tells Bob everything and paddles out to my grass hut in the jungle to set up housekeeping.

I wonder if he would care if she left him. He barely spends any time with her. I have a feeling they applied to the Peace Corps thinking they would escape whatever was wrong in their marriage and are now unconsciously trying to escape each other.

Well, she isn't going to find refuge under my wing.

Why can't women go to bed with you and leave it at that? They all believe in romance. Society has made them love addicts. Most men too. They've all heard and read so much about romantic love that it actually happens to them. They fall in love. And fall out of love. And then fall into love again.

Thank heaven I'm immune to that colossal waste of mental energy. Love, romantic love that is, was invented in twelfth-century Europe. It is not a universal human affliction, and that can be proved, historically and anthropologically. Love is a neurosis of so-called advanced civilization. Primitive peoples are clearheaded and honest enough to see that sex impulses have to do with sex and that marriage is a convenient way of conveying property, identifying parentage and, in some cases, rearing children.

It is amazing that an otherwise unself-deceiving person like Sarah doesn't see around the love propaganda. Look what believing in it has done to her life. It got her tied up with Bob. She fell in love with him, somehow, and never stopped to find out how he was in bed or at anything else. Now she hates him because he's dull all round.

Missy isn't any different, really. She's in love with me. Why me? She certainly must have had equally good sex with others before me. She doesn't need a linguist to earn money for her, not with her family. But I am positive she has been fantasizing about our blissful life together almost since the day we met. I'm sure she sits there in Cambridge denying her economy-size libido on my behalf and wishing she could think of a way to go with me to Qatab, where she would be totally wretched.

She probably expects me to propose to her this weekend.

July 20

FADE IN

1. EXTERIOR: LONG SHOT OF POOL   DAY

Track slowly in through grove of overhanging palms to poolside. Close in on HIM in black chinos and white button-down shirt with sleeves rolled up. He is looking thoughtfully down at the water.

                                                CUT TO

2. EXTERIOR: DOLLY SHOT OF POOL SURFACE   DAY

Track overhead as SHE swims underwater the entire length of the pool (from SR to SL) in long glides. SHE comes up for air as she turns and swims back to the other end of the pool where HE is waiting for her. SHE is wearing flowered bathing cap and pink one-piece bathing suit one size too small.

SHE (Voice Over):This must be 21. . . . After 20 laps you forget . . . enter a warm, dark world . . . covering you safely, smoothly, gliding over you. . . . You stretch longer and longer, like a rubber band, looser though, not tighter, looser all the time, out and out until you can reach from one end of the pool to the other.

                                                CUT TO

3. EXTERIOR: TWO SHOT AT POOL EDGE, SR   DAY

HE kneels down, when SHE reaches his end of the pool, and taps her on the shoulder. SHE starts to swim away angrily, but HE pulls her back.

SHE: Leave me alone. I was just beginning to forget you under there.

HE: I just came to say good-bye. I'm going now.

SHE (Hitching up the top of her suit): Three days without me on your back. I'll bet you're glad to get away.

CUT TO

4. EXTERIOR: MEDIUM CLOSE-UP OF HER FROM HIS POV
DAY

HE (Voice over): You make too much of everything, Sarah. We're not on stage or in a movie. Try to forget you're playing a scene in a romantic melodrama. It's only real life here.

SHE frowns and dives back into the water, gliding away.

CUT TO

5. EXTERIOR: POOLSIDE, FULL-LENGTH SHOT OF HIM
DAY

HE shrugs, turns and walks away from pool and off screen.

CUT TO

6. INTERIOR: INTERCITY BUS ON ROAD TO SAN JUAN   DAY

HE is crammed among a large family in the back of the bus. They are eating lunch—fried pig's ears—out of a paper bag. The MOTHER offers HIM an ear. HE hesitates. They all laugh as HE eats it. Random conversation in Spanish between HIM and family. More laughter.

FADE OUT

July 29

To: Mrs. Sinclair
From: William Macomber
Subject: Tallboy

This completes the special dossier for Tallboy. A decoded copy should be sent to Underlord as soon as possible along with blowups of the infrared photos. The camera worked perfectly, although I did rip my pants taking one of the shots. I had to replace the suit and am expensing it as an unreceiptable repair item on my official automobile.

I followed the volunteer to San Juan International Airport on July 26. He met a blond young woman who got off Pan American's flight Number 336 at 1322 hours. She had only hand luggage, a cylindrical canvas duffel bag probably purchased from L. L. Bean; so they left immediately by cab and went directly to the Miramar Hotel.

The airline identified her—she was the only unaccompanied woman on the flight—as Missy Rand. Documents in her handbag (see photos 7–9) identify her further as the daughter of Adelbert Rand, East Athol, Mass. He must be the former ambassador and, I believe, a major Democratic campaign contributor. Please check this as it could be of great interest to Underlord.

The Miramar cooperated fully with our investigation. Unfortunately Tallboy and Miss Rand spent most of the weekend on the beach and out of mike range. Bugged conversations recorded in the hotel room do not yield much of significance. The photographic evidence, however, is ideal.

Other than the above, I can only report that our young friends seem to have had one mild quarrel on Sunday morning. She cried briefly (see photo 378), but, inasmuch as they switched at that point to a language unknown to me, I cannot advise on specific content. The raw tape from that episode is being pouched separately. Perhaps you have someone who can make it out.

Kaufman will have to carry on from here, because the group moves out in two days, and I will have my hands full organizing that.

W.M.

(Decoded by S.McG.K.)

This transcript was prepared for us in New Delhi. The original dialogue was in an obscure language of the Hunza area. The delay in translation, necessitated by the primary difficulty of identifying the language and the secondary difficulty of finding a translator, was unavoidable and has rendered the material obsolete. S.McG.K. 1–25–64

MALE VOICE: Roll over. I'll scratch your back.

FEMALE VOICE: I don't want my back scratched. It's sunburned. How could you forget?

M.V.: Sorry.

F.V.: Talk to me instead. Tell me what you're thinking about.

M.V.: Not much. What a great time we're having.

F.V.: Please get your head out of there. I want to talk to you.

M.V. *(muffled)*: I can still talk.

F.V.: Come on. I'm serious.

M.V.: Too serious.

F.V.: Don't you feel this is an important moment?

M.V.: Every moment with you is important, my sweet.

F.V.: This is our last day together, you (untranslatable).

M.V.: I didn't get that last word.

F.V.: Never mind about it. What about our future.

M.V.: I thought that was all decided. I'll spend two years in Qatab. You'll be in medical school when I get back.

F.V.: And then what?

M.V.: I haven't planned that far. Have you?

F.V.: Look. I can't sit on the shelf for two years on the chance we might get back together.

M.V.: Well, I can't promise anything. Do what you like, but I refuse to make a blood pact.

F.V.: I knew you didn't care. *(Sobbing.) (Silence for three minutes.)*

M.V.: Feel better? . . . You can visit me during vacations. We can write. And maybe I'll feel more like committing myself soon, in a month, in a year. Who knows? It doesn't matter that much what we say we're going to do anyway.

July 29.   I wish I were still a virgin. They're all after my balls. Missy wanted to take them home with her in her Bean bag. She cried at the airport, as if it made any difference whether we were engaged or not during the next two years.

Then I returned to my tent and found Sarah loaded for bear. Somehow she found out I'd been with another woman. Didn't I feel any commitment or loyalty to her? Or love? She threat-

ened to tell Bob about us. I told her to go right ahead if she
wanted to. She was bluffing, naturally.

Only one more day.

July 29

Dear Alan,

I thought about you every minute of the trip back. I was very
silly Sunday morning. You were right, are right. It would have
been ridiculous to tie ourselves up for two years. I am no romantic heroine.

In fact, I have just finished spending the night with the man
who sat next to me on the plane. His name is Harold Metesky.
He is a city planner, recently divorced and lives in a big, empty
house in Arlington, which is quite convenient, as you can imagine. I don't think he'll ever master spoken Burushaski, but he
knows quite a few other things already.

Write me when you get to Qatab. I look forward to seeing you
at Christmas.

Thanks for the weekend,
Missy

July 30.   The list came from Washington. Everyone was selected. We fly to Chiotteville tomorrow via Trinidad. Somehow
the flight will last six hours. No news yet about specific assignments. We find out about them on the spot.

I feel absolutely prostrate with excitement. My stomach
seems to have been inflated with helium, stretched taut. Training made me forget what was going to happen afterward. In
only a few days, I'll be in a trackless jungle surrounded by
gibbering tapirs and camouflaged anacondas. For the first time
in about two years, I'll meet some people I can't talk to in their
own language, storybook savages, headhunters who eat missionaries and cover their crotches with leafy G-strings.

My job: teach them Shakespeare and how to wipe themselves.

July 31.   Air Qatab Flight 17 took off only one hour late from the San Juan airport. I wrote a crossword puzzle to keep my mind off the delay and to avoid having to sit at the bar with Sarah and Bob. It finally hit her this morning that she might have to live in a grass hut without plumbing for two years. So she's taking her last bath in rum.

On board: I'm on the aisle. Sarah is in the middle and Bob has the window. Does he suspect anything? For the first time I feel guilty.

The airplane must be a hand-me-down from Air France. So this is what happened to the prop planes when the big carriers switched over to jets. I hope they maintain them. Captain Oukuma, our trusty pilot, came aboard barefoot and dressed in a blue cotton robe. Sarah took one look at him, groaned, swigged from her tax-free Bacardi bottle and fell asleep leaning against me. Bob is trying to ignore her.

The stewardesses are very tiny and speak only Roucou. I can't make out a single word. They're very businesslike, though. They wear shoes and tailored suits in patch Madras. And lunch looked pretty much like any airline meal. Served on plastic trays. Except that the main dish was incredibly peppery. A sort of gumbo with okra. Beverage: corn beer. I wonder if Air Qatab employs old women to premasticate the grain for it in the classic manner. Tastes of mouth, definitely.

Trinidad: Two hours in a baking-hot transit lounge with no seats. Sarah spent most of the time in the john. I watched a fellow passenger and his wife and their baby waste an hour going through Trinidadian immigration. He is Korean, a karate instructor; she's Puerto Rican. Unfortunately, his passport is printed in Korean. No one knows what to do about that, and there is some problem about his hands being considered a lethal weapon in Trinidad. The appropriate form is missing. The baby yowls.

Qatab: We land on a single lane of crumbling asphalt. No

terminal building, just a big carport-style roof for protection against the rain. A fleet of 1947 (approx.) Peugeot taxis, all white, was there to take us in to Chiotteville. First, customs. Very strict. Conceivably for political reasons. Or is it racism?

A French traveling salesman blatantly bribed his way through. We noble Peace Corps volunteers endured the entire process, including a very thorough frisk for drugs. One middle-aged official with a yellow cigarette dangling from his lips searched everyone, men and women, one at a time, in a stifling, windowless room undecorated except by a poster of President Tukuna with the caption: "HAIL QATABIAN DEVELOPMENT." In French, English and Roucou. At last, a useful phrase in Roucou.

I repeat it to the official. "Ale'em Pritsak Qatabiminu."

"Take off all your clothes and bend over," he replies.

I comply. He probes my rectum with a rubber-gloved finger. I wonder if he finds much heroin that way.

Sarah's turn is next. She emerges pale but undeniably exhilarated. "If I ever come this way again," she says, "I'll try to remember to put something in there for him to find. Maybe a miniature American flag."

Oh, Sarah, you have your moments. If you'd only stop trying to be respectable so much of the time.

August 1. Morning in Chiotteville. First impressions. The temperature is quite bearable, in the mid-eighties and fairly dry. The Hôtel de Chasse is pleasant enough, a rambling creaky mahogany manse furnished almost entirely with stuffed jaguar heads and pictures of Tukuna in full flamingo regalia.

We drew up to the door in a disorderly caravan last night expecting the worst after 12 rutted miles in an antique Peugeot. The city begins gradually. It is hard to say just where the jungle ends and civilization takes over.

The demarcation is very abrupt at the airport. Forest like a wall at the perimeter of the tarmac. You plunge immediately into an infinite thicket. Mahogany knees at window level. The

ACROSS

1   Sounds like it's good for priests, but it's really no use unless you want to get married (7, 2, 6).

9   He gives you work for sassing (7).

10   Success associated with a bookish camp where they fed on air or grain (7).

11   Turn the pots around and then quit (4).

12   Gonzales poses a question (6, 4).

13   Indicate where to paint (5, 2).

15   Do birds swim here? Whether or not, the moon wanes as if bewitched (7).

17   One small boat holds a pair of twisted fins and Southern courtesy from stem to stern (7).

19   Takes on, you hear, the way some do with ease (7).

20   What's yin during Pentecost? Nothing's the same, and you have to forget about the band (10).

22   The beginning of a divine phone call (4).

25   One German in the arena, pulling back (7).

26   When god's blood flows, a Citroën drives up with flowers (7).

27   A shogun wings Teddy. Why, it's out of the question to stop now. This is one of those shindigs where a near miss means no miss (7, 8).

DOWN

1   Everything, to the British ear, is in the past tense, but in America the pulse runs faster. Is it our kidneys? (5).

2   Two plain men are worth one Christian in the East or an Estonian besieging Rome (9).

3   It tires you out, spilling gas south of Florence (4).

4   Honk your horn outside the Secret Service post and they'll think you're a rowdy drunk (7).

5   Framers of the Constitution didn't think they were an oppressed class (7).

6   Yes, pearls are tossed before swine when women throw themselves at men (4, 5).

7   Bitchy birds (5).

8   A Russian football cheer? It's also popular in Skoplje (9).

13   Do not fail to acquire the vocabulary entries at the end of the chapter for your own. They will get you

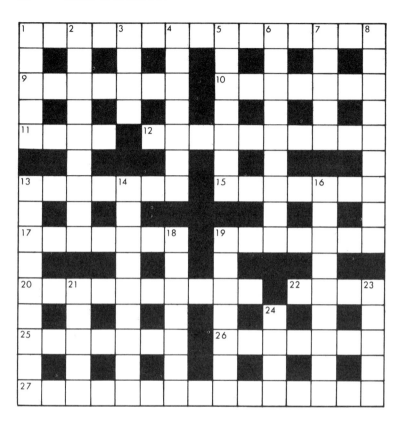

through many a tight spot. Take shibboleth, for
example (9).
14   The miller uses a cheap, thin grist and leaves the
baker parched (9).
16   In conclusion, the whole man must embrace even his
Spanish uncle (9).
18   Watch us pass arm in arm. Ain't she cute as a
pistol? (7).
19   A noble animal, the shellfish (7).
21   "I go in?" says Jones. "Maybe, but not headfirst."
(5).
23   Secret Army lives! In the Sahara (5).
24   Throwing dice around, you'll do no better than if
you'd sent Puck flying after your whim (4).

driver cursed in Roucou when a green and blue parrot smashed into the windshield, coating the glass with blood and feathers. We didn't stop, though, just barreled on.

The carcass rolled onto the right fender and stayed there, beak up, all the way in.

For eight miles, nothing but trees. Then one shack . . . a scattering . . . more. They looked like root beer stands, abandoned root beer stands, boxy slat walls, no windows—I mean no glass—just rectangular openings, corrugated-metal roofs, harlequin laundry steaming on the roofs. Mostly no people visible. Occasionally a black body in tatters would emerge to inspect the approaching din. Bush Negroes, authentic black militants who stopped serving whitey as soon as slavery ended. They just went back to the jungle and grew yams.

If the trees were less gargantuan and dense, this could be rural Georgia: wet and green, poor, almost uninhabited, except for the occasional weathered hut.

I sit up front with the driver. Bob and Sarah are in back with the luggage that wouldn't fit in the trunk. The driver wears a short-sleeved white shirt and nattily pressed white pants, no socks and white low-cuts—immaculate, a tennis pro. Close-cropped hair on a large boulder head. This must be a good job. He keeps a small transistor blaring the French hit parade. Sylvie Vartan, Les Haricots Rouges. A synthetic tiger's tail dangles from the rear-view mirror. We talk.

"In your country," he says in French that would make Antoine wince ("dans ton pays," the "tu" form right off the bat; is it friendliness or is that all they ever heard from their French overlords, every black addressed like a servant?), "do you know Addie Gems?"

"Addie Gems?"

"The trumpet player."

"Oh, yes, Harry James. I never met him, but I like his music."

"He plays well. Has many wives. White wives. Does that cause trouble? A black man with white wives?"

"But he's not . . . I mean, no, Mr. James is special."

I think of Bogart shipwrecked in North Africa. Rescued, he sits in the Bedouin chief's tent. The chief asks him, "Do you know Rita Hayworth?" The fruits of cultural supremacy.

We reach the city limits. Signs for the Lions, Rotary International and Moose. "175,132 INHABITANTS, 87,583 READERS OF PARIS MATCH." A chicken runs across the road. We are following a sagging Berliet diesel truck now, eating its exhaust. The street is narrow. Open concrete sewers run along one side, dry but littered with the day's garbage: bones, yellow citrus peels, empty packs of Gauloises bleues. Barefoot children play on the narrow sidewalk. We are close enough to touch them.

An old woman rounds the next corner balancing a basket on her head. The basket contains . . . sunglasses.

We pull into a small square, the Place Schoelcher, named after the man who got slavery abolished in the French Empire. A half-timbered church faces the Chiotteville branch of Aux Printemps. Sarah is still complaining about the toilet at the airport. Bob tries to pay no attention.

The driver—his license, taped to the dash, gives his name as Zouzou Macaire—continues his guided tour. We must visit the Musée National, but not on Wednesdays, when it is closed. Over there is Roger Garaudy, the most chic store in Chiotteville with the biggest selections of perfume and Swiss watches. Zouzou, however, has a friend who will give us 25 percent off, instead of 20, on traveler's checks.

Over a mahogany plank bridge (the Pont Tukuna), we cross the Mashmish, which is running high and turbid from the recently ended rainy season. It is gray, green and greasy, the New Limpopo. A string of bright orange and red and green and yellow fishing boats line the rocky banks below. They all have names painted on their prows: *Salvation, Flora, Ressac.*

Across the bridge, Zouzou waits to merge with the traffic circling the Place de l'Indépendance. In the center, a grove of ancient palms rise above a large parking lot. We zigzag through the laneless traffic and turn off onto the Boulevard Tukuna. A large sign proclaims: "HOTEL DE CHASSE, BERCEAU DE LA NATION, TOUS CONFORTS, EAU COURANTE."

Sleep came easily in the overstuffed bed. I tried to meditate on young François Tukuna clearing dishes downstairs in this hotel not so long ago, exciting himself with fantasies of omnipotence and rage.

Morning arrived as it should, with cocks crowing. Then a knock on the door. Breakfast: a big cup of café au lait, a rock-hard croissant and a magnificent grapefruit. And now, having shaken the scorpions out of my shoes and shaved with running but cold water, I must, I suppose, begin my mission.

IV

... GO FORTH

TO SERVE

August 2. Yesterday began with a mysterious phone message from a Mr. Kaufman. I was walking out of the lobby of the Hôtel de Chasse, about to take a walk around the city, when the French concierge caught up with me. He wanted me to leave my room key and, seeing the number, realized who I was.

The message had been taken the day before, but, in the rush of registering all of us, he had neglected to give it to me. He was very sorry. Still, Americans wanted things done so quickly. Could I please pay cash for the phone call?

Naturally, I had no risps yet. The concierge looked sad and swatted a yellow spider crawling on his knee. The spider squashed into a red stain on his black pants. He motioned me to the phone booth and put the call through. An embassy operator answered. Kaufman came on. Philadelphia accent. Problems with my assignment. Could I drop by today at noon? We could discuss it all over lunch at Le Bagne, "the only good French bistro in town."

I started out the door again. Sarah and Bob caught me this time. Could I help them house-hunt? They had just heard they were assigned to Chiotteville. She was going to be a teacher; he would be advising the government health insurance program. I told them about Kaufman. Then we walked two blocks

through burning sun and swarms of flies to the Agence Im-
mobilière Holzmann.

Holzmann *fils* was behind the counter, round and hairless,
eyebrows and lashes bleached to transparency, a eunuch
flanked by a harem of three black secretaries. I explained our
mission. He had just the thing, a villa belonging to an old lumbering family, the Aloyaus, who intended the house eventually
for one of their 13 children. It was built on a hill overlooking
the sea, still rested on its original mahogany pilings and boasted
a freshly dug outhouse. Rent: 75 risps plus two months' security
and 12 percent of the annual rent as a commission for our friend
Holzmann. Another couple, from the Liberian Embassy, were
coming in an hour to give a deposit. He would naturally rather
rent to Sarah and Bob, who would "appreciate the house's historical meaning so much better than those Africans," but they
would have to act quickly.

He neglected to mention that the road leading to the house
was a slough preceded by a canton of hovels at the foot of the
hill or that the "rustique" furniture looked ripe for fumigation
or that the new outhouse had blown over during the rainy
season. Electricity there was. And cold water from the tap,
though not potable because "those niggers down there" (ces
nègres en bas) had fouled the well. But you couldn't find clean
water anywhere in the whole country.

Sarah liked the view and pushed Bob into signing a letter of
agreement. No lease. That would force the Aloyaus to report
the income to the Qatab tax department, which delighted in
penalizing Europeans. We would find out about that.

I pointed out that we weren't Europeans. Holzmann said it
all came down to the same thing, either you came from a race
with a history or you didn't.

Sarah had a point about the view. From the veranda, you
looked out on water that was so perfect it looked like something
else, a vast plain of flashing crystal illuminated from below. The
house perched on the edge of a sheer cliff riotous with vegeta-

tion. If you fell over it, you would impale yourself on grapefruit trees or mangoes. A gang of glaring orange flowers carpeted the ground and sent up a perfume strong enough to sell at Woolworth's. At the horizon, a fishing boat hove into view.

The Ashtons move in tomorrow. Liberia loses again, and I get invited to dinner.

First came lunch with the oleaginous Mr. Kaufman. I say oleaginous because he glistened and because he moved across his office to greet me as if he were sliding or rolling on skates. A tiny pearl of sweat hung from his chin. Kaufman was only a second secretary, but he must still be eating well. He bulged with well-being and smiled with jowls and dewlaps as I sat down in a Barcelona chair across from his glass desk. He wore a three-piece Glen plaid lightweight suit. The vest had its own set of lapels. And on his feet Kaufman wore a pair of patent-leather pumps, cracked but shiny.

He caught me staring at them and excused himself: "I wear them in the office, because they're so comfortable. And they help me remember what it was like to be in a civilized country." I waited for him to get to the point. Instead, he put out his cigar and motioned me to the door.

Le Bagne is, as the name implies, tricked out to look like a prison, like *the* prison on the Île d'Enfer just offshore from Chiotteville, where France sent her criminal dregs for 150 years. The restaurant is all gray inside and divided into cells with sliding doors and barred windows. The maître d' locked us in. A menu was slid through the bars by a waiter in guard's uniform. Bread and water were already on the table. So were a file and a length of rope.

The menu billed itself as "Le Dernier Repas." But the dishes advertised were no joke. I let Kaufman order. We began with an omelet stuffed with sea urchin eggs. Outside, the egg was a deep satisfying yellow flecked with brown. Inside, just inside the thin outer layer, it ran in thick gold streams that hid the rich musky darkness of the oeufs d'oursin. Wine was pushed through the bars, in a carafe. The food was all served in tin dishes on trays pushed under the door by a boy in an executioner's out-fit, buff jerkin and black hood with eyeholes. We ate with spoons.

The second course was a langouste à la parisienne standing erect as a sentinel on a bed of morels in cream. Kaufman ate his quickly and plied me for gossip from Harvard Square. He had graduated in '54 from the College, with a *cum* in fine arts. I kept him at bay with that hoary joke about a print in the Fogg Museum being worth two in the Busch. He hadn't heard it but countered with a story about a clubby roommate of his who liked to go up to Cliffies in the museum and ask: "Where in the Fogg am I?"

Next came what seemed like pork in a brown sauce with onions. It was suckling tapir, sauce Robert. The meat was faintly high. The sauce was a mirror. As we finished and were mopping up the last drops with pieces of hardtack, Kaufman leered across at me and asked if I had ever heard of the Xixis.

"Only what I read in a Peace Corps poop sheet, and that wasn't much."

"I wrote that," Kaufman beamed. "We still don't know much, but we would very much like to know more."

"And I'm your man. Is that it?"

"More or less. We've tried everything else. The government can't make contact with them. They don't recognize its author-ity. Missionaries have never made headway there. And the Xixis —you are not to repeat this to anyone—are sitting on the largest deposit of U–235 in the world.

"An early explorer brought back samples in 1785, when no one was interested. They moldered in a dusty display case at the Musée de l'Homme in Paris, as if they were artifacts, until two years ago, when the South American exhibits were updated. An astute curator sent out three suspiciously heavy rocks for analy-sis. Pure U–235. Three months later, a covert geological ex-ploration team reported back from the field that the principal

Xixi settlement, a village of 800, is perched on a seven-acre hill of the same stuff. They all should have died of radiation poisoning, so it is assumed that over the generations they have built up some kind of immunity.

"At any rate, the General immediately fired the man at the Rue Oudinot who had been the architect of Qatab's independence, and he is now pulling every string to get a mining concession in the pays du Xixi. Tukuna knows there is something funny in that. He would like to euchre what he can out of the French, but he's being wary. And to preserve his even-handed posture in international circles, he's announced that all countries are welcome to give technical assistance in developing the extreme south, where the Xixis are.

"That's a fairly hollow offer at the moment. There's no one who can speak the language. Rumors about headhunting Xixis continue to circulate. And Tukuna won't guarantee the safety of any expedition. He can't, of course. He has a standing army of three hundred, a palace guard who might as well be carrying blowguns. They are completely untrained.

"The French have offered to train an invasion force or to send in 'advisers' to clean out the Xixis. There are only a few thousand of them down there, total. We've made a similar offer as well. But Tukuna won't permit it. He may be holding out for a better deal. Actually, I think he just wants more information. No one has told him yet why the Xixi sector is so interesting. And you can't blame him for wanting us to explain why Paris and Washington are both suddenly fired up about 25,000 square miles of impassable, unmapped jungle.

"Privately, I am convinced we are going to have to spill the beans and hope for the best. He is going to find out eventually. He has no use for uranium himself; he'll have to find a buyer. We are a better customer than France. We were never involved here as a colonial power. Really, we hold all the trumps. But we've got to be able to convince him we can get in there peacefully. He won't buy an invasion and neither will my people at the moment. They're planning something much bigger in Southeast Asia.

"What I need . . . what the United States needs is someone clever enough to make friends with the Xixis and get them to agree to a mine."

"You mean you want someone to infiltrate, win the hearts of the Xixis and then buy their land for twenty-four dollars' worth of trinkets?"

"Don't be so cynical. You're too young. Oh, look, here is our vegetable course. I don't think it will fit under the door."

It was a soufflé, high and puffy, accompanied by an orange sauce. The executioner summoned a turnkey. With clubs drawn they brought in the dish and served it. It was an asparagus soufflé, green as balsam, with a sauce maltaise, orange-flavored hollandaise on the side, served in a skull.

We ate silently and I thought quickly that I could refuse to cooperate and suffer the consequences (a draft call? expulsion from the Peace Corps?) or accept but refuse to cooperate at the end of my tour. Could I pull that off? Probably not. Supposing I established myself in a Xixi village and learned the language and made friends. That would be enough proof to Tukuna (and to the Xixis) that Americans were OK. The mine concession would be agreed upon. I would be irrelevant from there on out. And the Xixis would go the way of the Sioux and the Blackfeet.

Dessert came, a mangue bourdaloue, mangoes and pastry cream on a buttery tart crust glazed with guava jelly. I smiled at Kaufman. He smiled at me.

"I won't do it," I said. "Find another stooge."

Kaufman kept eating his tart. He finished and pulled his brief-case up onto his lap.

"It's elephant skin," he explained. "I bought it for practically nothing from an Indian moneychanger when I was working in Saigon."

He pulled out a manila envelope and passed it to me. Inside were glossy 8 x 10s of two people without clothes performing an intimate act. Their faces were turned conveniently forward, toward the camera. Missy and I had put on quite a show.

"Whoever he is does very nice work," I said.

"You can keep them if you like," Kaufman replied, "since the negatives are very safe."

"What's my official assignment?" I asked, stalling, hoping I could figure out some way to stop this nightmare.

"I knew you would see the light. I am happy to announce that you have been chosen to introduce modern sanitation methods to the Xixis. Your destination is a small village at the headwaters of the Mashmish, within sight of the Tumuc-Humac. No outsider has visited there since 1835. It's called Kuva."

"Is the CIA going to issue me a lead loincloth?"

"We picked the village because it is twenty kilometers away from the uranium."

"As far as you know."

"As far as we know. But you will be given a radiation detector in case we're wrong. The main point of the exercise is to create a beachhead. We'll expect you to establish friendly relations with them, explain the American way to them and write a dictionary. You will be free to leave at the end of two years. But by that time we hope to have the mine in operation."

"And if I fail?"

"You would probably not want the American Linguistics Association to know that you were unable to put together a simple word list, would you? And I can guarantee that Ambassador Rand will see those pictures of you and his daughter."

"I could probably survive not marrying her."

"But you won't survive Adelbert Rand. He has enough clout to make you unemployable in any university in America."

"You bastard. How am I supposed to do all this anyway? I mean, if no one else has managed to cozy up to the Xixis in two centuries, how could I?"

"You have Ituru."

"That's right. Natural ituru. Without it, I wouldn't be where I am today."

"Ituru is the son of a Xixi chief. He was adopted—to be honest about it, he was kidnaped—by a Methodist missionary who tried to convert him. The missionary died ten years ago, but Ituru stayed in Chiotteville as a ward of the embassy. He speaks basic English and Creole and, of course, Xixi. His twenty-first birthday is tomorrow. He wants to return to his people. He'll take you in."

"When do we leave?"

"That's the problem we're meeting to discuss. The Tukuna government hasn't approved the Peace Corps sanitation program yet. As soon as it passes the Cabinet, you and Ituru push off."

"Meanwhile we wait?"

"Meanwhile you wait."

Kaufman and I finished our coffee. He lit a cigar. The executioner opened the cell door and we walked out into the blazing Chiotteville afternoon. Kaufman told me not to call him. He would be in touch as soon as the plan was ready. There would be plenty of time for me to get to know Ituru on the trip to Kuva.

I kept on walking, past the hotel, feeling trapped and logy from lunch and sweaty from the heat. I obviously can't write Missy about this; they must be opening my mail. I wonder how long that's been going on? It's funny, I guess. I'm getting to do exactly what I wanted: lose myself in a remote, primitive village with an unknown language. But it's not my plan any more. Not subversive or un-American or any kind of escape. Unless I can wriggle out of the net later on. Greenspan would know what to do, but how can I reach him?

August 3.   No message from Kaufman. I loitered in the lobby waiting, practiced Roucou with the doorman-bootblack-bellhop, exchanged dollars for risps at the bank around the corner, helped some other Volunteers move their bags into cabs that were taking them toward their assignments, tried to think of a better "12 Across" for my puzzle, sent Missy a card with a picture of a flamingo on it (Dear M.,/ Congratulations on your rebound./I await marching orders./Rumor has it I will dig latrines./ Love,/A.), and went out at 12:30 looking for lunch. Wandered down toward the Mashmish in the direction of cheering and whistling. Turned into a sort of courtyard, really an alley between two peeling houses and found a crowd of men in work clothes (threadbare shorts, no shirts, barefoot) watching a cockfight. Betting system very complicated. Odds go up if you put money on a wounded cock. Man in a green turban holds money and has to remember all the bets and odds. How can he do it? Mnemonic skill of the illiterate? Before the fight, trainers show off cocks, preen them, boast of prowess. Small boys open leather cases and sharpen spurs, then attach them. Cocks thrown at each other. I put 50 kalpans on mean-looking rooster missing one toe, a veteran with a lavish spray of green feathers. His opponent is slightly smaller. Fight very fast. Birds leap at each other, seem to bounce off ground a yard or so, to gain height advantage, slash at the other one's neck on the way down. Plumage flashes gold and green and indigo as they feint and screech and flap and fly off at oblique angles. In 15 seconds, it's over. My cock lies in a pool of blood and feathers. They bring out another pair. Turban collects more risps and kalpans. I bet again, lose again.

On the way out, I buy a glass of corn beer and a piece of flat bread from a vendor. Beer is yeasty and flat. The bread—must have been manioc flour—is pasty. The vendor fries it in a cut-off oil drum over a wood fire.

Back at the H. de Chasse, no message. A hunting party arrives fresh from the bush. Americans with big guns, faces covered with sting welts, looking for a taxidermist. Everyone out to lunch. They ask me if I know where the kitchen is. Their jaguar is high already and they want to refrigerate it to keep it from falling apart. One of them pulls me over to a big canvas bag and opens drawstring. Bloody, spotted heap inside. Eyes look out blankly. We drag to kitchen. Small, prewar box, a Norge, is almost empty but the "jag bag," as one of the hunters calls it, won't fit inside. I leave them in disgust, go up to my room and take a nap.

6 P.M. It is still hot. I change my clothes and take a cab up to Sarah's house. I try my Roucou on the driver. He seems surprised I can speak it and asks me if I'm going to the President's speech tomorrow. Tukuna is dedicating a new hospital. Worth seeing.

Sarah must have heard the cab. She comes out to meet me. There is a flamingo on the lawn. Very LMC, I think, but at least she had the good sense not to buy a statue of a black coachman. Then the flamingo flew away. Sarah and I embrace. Bob is at a meeting. We have an hour.

The bedroom is stifling. Sarah hasn't had a chance to bathe and smells ripe. She covers me with thighs and moist buttocks, screaming with pleasure. No need to whisper up here on this hill away from everyone.

Suddenly, silence. Sarah stops bucking and rolling. I pull my head out from under her and see Bob in the doorway. He stands there for a moment, blank, and walks out. We get dressed. I wipe my face off with the bedspread. We walk downstairs. Bob has poured himself a drink. His hand is shaking and he spills half of it as he moves toward a chair. He sits down and the chair collapses sending Bob, in a long sprawl and splash of whiskey, to the floor. I help him up. He stands and then moves to slap me. I duck out of the way. He covers his face with his hands and mumbles hoarsely: "Get out." I walk out the door and down the hill. It takes 45 minutes to reach the hotel.

August 2

Dear Alan,

I hope you are enjoying Qatab. Here in Arlington, it is very quiet and I am studying for my chem. final. Metesky keeps me busy all night.

I miss you very much.
Love,

Missy

August 4. L'Hôpital Tukuna was thrown up in the record time of six months on the parade field of the old French garrison headquarters. It was easy to find. I just fell in with a pack of schoolchildren. As we neared the hospital, a klaxon sent us all jumping into the sewer trenches of the narrow, one-lane street. A black Citroën DS limousine with tinted windows raced by, motorcycle outriders fore and aft. You could not see who was inside, but the children recognized the car and the meaning of the escort. They began chanting "Tukuna-na-na, Tukuna-na-na," and did not stop until we reached a machine-gun check-point at the entrance to the parade grounds. The children skipped inside, unhindered and unconcerned.

As I approached, a machine gunner pointed his weapon straight at me. I froze, and three soldiers came forward. One went through my passport while the other two frisked me. Soon, they waved me on, sullenly.

The ceremony took place on the steps of the hospital. It could not have been held inside the white, square stucco building because there would have been no room for the crowd, which must have numbered several thousand. Even so, a few white faces stood out in the black multitude, and I was able to pick out Kaufman's natty sphere of a body close to the dais. I made my way to him.

"Good morning, Mr. Kaufman."

"So you've decided to take an interest in local politics?"

"Not exactly. I had nothing else to do, and I seem to remember that my assignment falls in the area of health. Why shouldn't I visit a hospital?"

"No reason at all. In fact, this might be a good chance for you to meet Ungburu, the minister who looks after public health. He's the one we have to convince about you.

"Look up there. It's our leader."

François Tukuna strode out of the main entrance, tall and majestic in royal-blue robe and flamingo headdress. He had not smeared his face with red pigment—this was a minor celebration—but the initiation scars showed clearly on his cheeks, jagged and stretching from ears to chin.

The crowd chanted "Tukuna-na-na" in unison until he raised his arms over them and bade them sit. Silent in an instant, they fell to the ground and the speech began.

"O Qatabians—Roucous, Ufas, Xixis, Bush Negroes, Farfallas and Sintulus, Kraithi, Miltyuk and Saras, Boros and Jiks, my children—in the long trek toward our national destiny, we have faced and conquered hordes of enemies, powerful foes greater in numbers and might than ourselves. We have vanquished danger from without and dissension from within. We are, however, still standing watch against our enemies to the west who shall be ever nameless and accursed. And we must also never relax our vigilance against attack from North Americans lusting for our natural riches or from Europeans still smarting from old wounds and hungry for plunder.

"For all this we must remain strong. And to be strong we must be healthy. We must learn not only to survive human invasions, but also to triumph over sickness. This beautiful hospital is an important step in that direction. It is equipped with the most modern equipment. It is air-conditioned. It has two physicians, one surgeon and fifteen nurses. [Cheers and whistles from the crowd.]

"To build it, my government paid fifteen million risps, eight risps for every man, woman and child. And we give it to you, for your use all of your days, regardless of tribe or clan, sex or station. I speak to you in Roucou, but I speak for all.

"This great hospital will heal many of you, but even a child can see that it will not hold all who are sick. We only begin our campaign against disease here today. Tomorrow we press on to build more, learn more, fight more, for a healthier country, for all Qatabians, for all of you."

The crowd shouted and whistled and began to disperse. I felt Kaufman tugging at my shoulder.

"The Honorable Mr. Ungburu is over there," he said.

We started pushing toward a small, wizened young man in a wash-and-wear suit. Kaufman reached him first and introduced me in French. The minister smiled dourly.

"We do not believe, we in this humble country, that white men have magic powers. We think that white men are as weak as we are before nature. Therefore, young man, we see no value in permitting you to expose yourself to the dangers of the pays du Xixi. Where we have failed, you will not succeed unless you have supernatural powers. Do you have supernatural powers, young man?"

"No, sir," I replied in Roucou. "only natural powers."

"And much optimism."

"Yes. I want to see for myself."

A voice from behind me broke in: "Who is this white boy who speaks our language?" I turned and saw Tukuna.

"An American," said Ungburu. "He thinks he can sanitize the Xixis."

"Someone will have to," said Tukuna. "Why not him? He asks nothing in return except friendship from us. What is your name, son, and how did you learn Roucou?"

"Alan Casper, Mr. President. In this city, talking with people."

"Will you talk with one more for a moment?"

Tukuna drew me along with him through the crowd. Shaking hands as he went, he spoke to me in French: "Ungburu knows nothing, but I have my reasons for appeasing him. He is afraid that the Peace Corps will succeed where he has failed. Ungburu's amour-propre does not concern me when important things are at stake. It is a useful weakness for those of us who understand him. I will tell him you are a fool, that you will certainly fail to clean up a single Xixi hut, but that it is important to me to acquire dollars for international transactions, which is true, and that the Peace Corps's presence helps to encourage tourism.

"Two words of advice. Go slowly with the Xixis and believe nothing of what your Mr. Kaufman says. I employ such serpents myself and recognize them instantly."

I was dismissed. The presidential entourage swept onward. Kaufman caught up with me slightly out of breath.

"Did he decorate you with the Order of the Golden Jaguar?"

"Yes, and he invited me to join him and the Cabinet for poker next Tuesday. Actually, he just made small talk and wished me luck among the Xixis."

"That means he's behind us."

"I think so."

"Let me buy you a farewell drink."

He drove me to the hotel and we went into the bar. Bob was there. Drunk. He saw me come in and started to leave. Then he turned back and came over to me. Livid. I got up off the bar stool. And caught Bob just as he was about to fall.

"Leggome. I'm geng ou thish plaish," he muttered. Kaufman helped me drag him to a booth.

"Bob, I'm sorry," I said.

"You wan er, you got er."

"Bob, you're making a mistake. I'm leaving town almost immediately. You can start over. I promise I'll stay away."

Kaufman and I carried him out to Kaufman's car. He passed out in the back seat. On the way to Bob's house, Kaufman fulminated against the Peace Corps's shoddy selection procedures, which didn't make sense because he was too smart to believe that Bob's present condition could have been predicted during training. Bob wasn't basically unstable; he was upset about me and his wife. Anyone could have figured that out by listening to him in the bar. Kaufman was inventing an excuse for me. I was his protégé and he wasn't going to let anyone cause me trouble. I hoped the Ashtons would come out of this

all right, but with Bob passing out in bars and Kaufman anxious
to protect my good name, they couldn't expect much help from
the United States government. I certainly couldn't help. My
situation was impossible. I was up to my eyes in complications.
There was no position I could take.

I stayed in the car while Kaufman helped Bob inside.
Slouched down to keep out of sight, I could see him talking to
Sarah at the door. We drove back to the hotel without talking.
I got out and spent the day buying a fishing rod and other
last-minute supplies for my trip.

August 5. Sarah called, very calm, calmer, in fact, than she
usually was. Bob had decided to stay—after a talk with "that
man from the embassy, Kaplan." He didn't want to disgrace the
United States or go back with a bad record from the Peace
Corps. I told her I thought we had better not meet before I
went away. She agreed so quickly I knew she had made the
decision before she phoned.

"I enjoyed it, Sarah," I said lamely.

"Don't remind me," she snapped. "Just don't make things
worse. I'm stuck with him. He's too weak to just drop like a used
Kleenex."

"Good-bye."

"Be careful."

After lunch, Kaufman sent a messenger for me. I walked to
the embassy and waited 20 minutes to get into his office. He
apologized as I entered. Washington had called.

I sat down in the ·Barcelona chair. The pumps were up on the
desk.

"Ungburu called. It's fine. He said his ministry had decided
to 'suffer fools with gladness.' " If I wanted to go, I could go. But
I shouldn't call him for help later on.

There had also been a letter from President Tukuna's personal secretary wishing me well and offering assistance.

It was time to meet Ituru. Kaufman buzzed his secretary, and in he came. Sallow, almost Oriental, Ituru stood only five feet high. His forehead was high, a bronze dome overhanging the narrow clerestory eyes. His nose had been broken in one place. The nostrils flared. The teeth in front were filed to sharp points. He wore fatigues and American tennis shoes.

We shook hands. "Do you have a raincoat?" he asked.

"No."

"Get one. Without it you'll drown. Buy two, in fact, in case one tears. Get the rubber kind with a hood. Put silicone spray on all your shoes. Buy a waterproof container for important papers. Your inoculations are O.K., I assume, but be sure you take twice as many malaria pills as you think you'll need. We leave tomorrow."

"Thank you, Ituru. I'm glad to know all that. How long will it take to get to Kuva?"

"Five days, if we're lucky and if they let us. Kuva isn't my village, but I have clan relatives there. My clan is the frog clan. We don't eat or even touch frogs.

"I'll meet you at the airport tomorrow at 6 A.M. Meanwhile practice the Xixi word for frog. Hamp'atu."

He repeated the word several times, making a guttural clicking noise with a rising tone where the apostrophe comes in the word. He smiled when I tried to imitate him and left.

"He doesn't seem too happy about going with me," I said to Kaufman.

"It's not your fault. He's afraid they'll make him get married if he goes back to his people. His bride was picked out years ago. The Xixis practice polyandry, so there are never enough men to go around." Kaufman noticed me smiling and frowned.

"Hamp'atu," I said and went to look for a pair of raincoats.

V

VOYAGE TO THE END

OF THE MASHMISH

August 7.   Oh my God but I am far from any golden room and fine talk now. We paddle—they paddle, I should say, the two lithe machines we hired along with their pirogue at Gé—35 miles a day, upstream. In three days, barring mishaps at rapids, we will reach Kuva. Ituru sits in front of me, silent as an obsidian statue. At lunch, he gives me my daily Xixi lesson, after which he turns to stone again. Is this the Xixi manner or is Ituru a casualty of cultural schizophrenia? I'll find out soon. The paddlers are Ufas. They chatter musically among themselves and wear green sarongs. They are parrots; Ituru's a glossy rock; and I'm a monkey, buff-colored, gregarious, a clown for the rest of the jungle.

I fall out of the canoe at a ford. My wet clothes, hung from the gunwales, slip off into the olive waters and sweep downstream behind us. They are lost, for under the tepid, smooth surface of this part of the Mashmish lurk piranhas and caymans and snakes, which no one will brave for the sake of a Lacoste shirt.

We flew to Gé, the southernmost landing point in Qatab, in a tiny old single-engine hydroplane. South of there the river is too rocky for pontoons, too shallow and plunging. At Gé civilization truly ends. My only link with the outside world, the shortwave rig from Kaufman, is strapped to the dugout in its crate. I am to use it only in emergencies.

For now, the only thing that matters is the pirogue, an 18-foot log hollowed out by hand, shaped for maximum speed and cargo capacity, hell to lift (and lift it we do, all four of us, grunting around rapids, stumbling under its weight, tripping on hidden, trailing lianas) and beautiful. Each chisel stroke that formed our boat left a line the eye can linger over, and those lines join together in a pattern of inexactness tending toward a curve but preserving the uneven pressures of the human hand.

And so we push on, looking, except for my presence, like a diorama in the American Museum of Natural History come to life. Someone has kissed the frog-prince, Ituru, and set him in demonic motion. No, he remains still but impels the world backward through sheer concentration.

And the world is become wood and water, two opposed and mysterious numina symbolizing stasis and movement. The mahogany trunks stretch up and up and hide the sky. At eye level, their giant roots with wizened bark reach into the water and down under the mud to unknown levels, unshakable pilings. My arms will not reach all the way round the trunks. They do not sway in the wind, nor do they seem to die. We have not sighted a fallen trunk in two days.

The trees are numberless, stretching in unbroken ranks up and down the river for a thousand miles, or so it seems, and looming over the earth in a giant grove, immobile and almost infinite, ancient and awful.

Only the river is free, always changing but always the same, running away from this dark-walled prison to the now barely imaginable openness of the sea. Against instructions, I secretly drop my hand in the turbid flow. The river meets my grasp, presses warmly against my palm. I feel something rough brush against me in the water and pull back, which makes the stern paddler, who has been watching me, giggle.

I try to fish, trolling, with spiders as bait. My catch consists of snagged branches and a dead frog. Ituru takes this as a bad omen. He fishes, to counteract my transgression, and lands an eel a yard long with mean fangs, which the bowman bludgeons with his paddle. At lunchtime, we pull up to a sandspit. Ituru stretches the eel out on the bank and nails it taut to the ground with sharpened twigs. He skins it and then chops flesh and bone into three-inch sections. He and the paddlers devour it raw and spit the bones into the river. I roast my portion. It tastes sweet.

We glide onward. Rains of wild ferocity hit us for five minutes at a time every hour or so, leaving all my clothes damp. There are two inches of water in the middle of the pirogue. I use my shirt as a sponge and squeeze the bilge over the side, while the paddlers continue to paddle, 15 strokes per minute, 900 strokes per hour, 9,000 strokes per day.

August 8.   No rain today. Clothes dried. Impossible to sleep last night. Tent too damp. Made up for it by napping on and off all day today. Bowman killed a sloth the size of a lamb. Meat for the rest of the trip.

August 9.   The river has narrowed. Rapids more frequent. We arrive tomorrow, Ituru says. Shaved for the first time during trip in anticipation. Hands blistered, and too exhausted from carrying pirogue to write.

August 10.   Morning: We are very shipshape now. I have been covering our packs with my raincoats. Life is much drier, although the rain continues to knock us flat ten times a day. Every once in a while, the forest breaks for a few hundred yards, revealing the Tumuc-Humac Range in the distance, gray peaks, the dark side of the moon.

Even so, I feel very happy. My life is radically simplified. Kaufman, Missy, Sarah, Bob and the linguistics community are all on some other planet. If I thought, which I seem to remember vaguely doing the day we left Chiotteville, that my life was

a mess of bollixed relationships and that it was hopelessly com-
promised by complicity in the uranium scheme, that mood has
passed.

I am part of the forest now. Someday I will have to return to
"civilization," but that is two years off. Until then, I am a Xixi
and nothing from out there can touch me.

4 P.M.: We pass another pirogue. Xixis. Ituru talks to them and
changes from stone to flesh, smiling and waving good-bye. Suddenly more pirogues: a greeting party. Men naked except for
woven penis shields. We round a bend. Kuva is on both sides of
us stretching up the banks. Neat huts on stilts. We beach the
pirogue on the right bank and prepare to get out. I must stop
writing for now. Great tumult. A scene from the *National Geo-
graphic*. Bare breasts of all shapes and sag. Fantastic painted
faces, spears, blowguns, everyone gathering at the water's edge.
Drums beat in the middle distance.

August 11

Dear Missy,

This is the last chance I will have to get mail out of here for
weeks or even months. Excuse me, I forgot I didn't explain that
we arrived in Kuva—my village—last night; it seems so inevitable now that I should be here that I assumed you knew already.
At any rate, my paddlers are about to head back downstream
as soon as the sun rises. Since they are Ufas, whose territory lies
to the northeast, they won't step foot on Xixi lands for fear of
violent reprisals. The Xixis have an evil reputation downriver,
although I have to say that my reception couldn't have been
more gracious and friendly.

Most of the gaiety, however, must have been in honor of my
guide and companion, Ituru, who has returned to his people
after several years in Chiotteville, a place so distant in the minds
of the Xixis—and in my mind too after our surreal boatride up
the Mashmish—that he might as well be returning from Paris.
Kuva is not his village (he leaves for there tomorrow on foot),

but all the Xixis are related in one way or another through an elaborate kinship system which I don't fully understand yet, and members of his clan, called hamp'atu or frog, led the celebration of our arrival. The chief, Warramunga, is also a hamp-'atu, which may have helped turn the evening into a real blowout.

Warramunga stands taller than any of his subjects (but a foot shorter than I; children and some adults kept pointing at me in awe all evening) and projects great dignity for someone clad in nothing but a penis shield. His face, like all the men's, is stippled with blue holes arranged to form a circle centered on each cheek. His hair is cut short, which emphasizes the high, beetling forehead characteristic of the tribe.

Warramunga does not appear to talk much. I learned enough Xixi from Ituru on the way up here, however, to pick up the sense of some of what he says, which is all quite official-sounding. You know, "Welcome to the land of the Xixis, O brave young man and friend of our long-lost Ituru, the bold traveler." That kind of stuff.

I made a decent stab at answering the old man (he looks old, but I have no idea about his age), which amused the other Xixis, because they are linguistically naïve and can't comprehend that a grown man would not know how to express himself properly in their language. I don't think they've had more than a handful of non-Xixi visitors here in anyone's lifetime; so their concept of other cultures is not highly developed. In other words, you are assumed to be a Xixi unless proved otherwise, and that goes even for white giants like me.

Which isn't as bizarre as it sounds. Look at the French, who are fundamentally unable to believe that foreigners don't know French perfectly. And so the typical tourist suffers because the natives think, unconsciously, that visitors are showing bad manners by obstinately continuing to babble in some inferior brogue.

The Xixis, of course, have more justification for this attitude than the French. And yet they are also very welcoming. I can't handle their horrendously difficult agglutinative grammar (like Hungarian, it tacks words and meaningful particles onto the basic root), and I haven't perfected a certain crucial clicking sound yet, but, even so, Warramunga seems to have adopted me into his clan.

I don't know what the implications of that are yet, because I don't understand how the clan system functions, but I think it was probably too confusing for them to deal with the idea of a guest (Ituru arranged with Warramunga that I should stay in Kuva indefinitely in return for my people's hospitality toward him in Chiotteville) who had no local totem or relatives in the village and who, therefore, had a life without meaning in the Xixi sense. So he adopted me, by a mere tap on the shoulder. I am living in his house with his other unmarried children as well as the children of his co-husbands. One immensely fat matriarch actually owns the house and cohabits there with her offspring and her three husbands, of whom Warramunga is the most important. All four adults are physically middle-aged and have married off all but two of their children, twin girls of 9. We all sleep in one room with a dirt floor and no furniture other than sleeping mats and cooking utensils. I am now sitting outside in front of the house, on a narrow veranda. The rest of my "family" are still sleeping off last night's feast.

At dinnertime yesterday, Warramunga took Ituru and me for a walk to the edge of the village, where the jungle begins. He had a scrawny male goat tethered there, cropping the underbrush. It must have been his pet, because it licked his hand, but Warramunga showed no remorse when he led it by a short liana halter back to the center of the village and slit its throat. A teenage girl named Suri caught the blood in an earthenware bowl, while Warramunga held the animal in the air by the hind legs.

After the last blood had trickled out of the jugular, Warramunga gave his knife to Suri and turned the goat upside down. She cut off balls and cock, letting them splash into the blood, and then she carried the bowl away.

By this time, a pit had been dug, a wood fire built and two stout posts driven into the ground at either end of the fire. Warramunga finished cleaning the goat and skinning it, at which point, Mrs. Warramunga, Cheqchiku, trundled over with a very large bowl of mush and two eggs. She poured the mush into the goat's cavity. Warramunga put in the eggs (as testicle surrogates?) and sewed up the cavity with what I think was a length of dried gut. Then, they skewered the goat, from throat to butt, with a long pole.

Onto the fire he went (his viscera, hide and head were just left there for the delectation of bugs and bacteria—that has got to stop), and while he roasted we drank a vile corn beer. Everyone was quite high in a few minutes, and then they began chewing coca leaves, which were passed by Cheqchiku. The barbecue rapidly turned into a piece of slapstick, especially when it came time to turn the goat, a cumbersome operation requiring several hands and extra sticks to prop the animal on his side. Cheqchiku periodically basted him with a very potent hot sauce. Little children were recruited to pee on the fire when it flamed up too high. They asked me to do it too, since I am technically a child here; I haven't gone through the initiation rite. And so I peed on the fire. Suri, having disposed of her bloody burden, stood at the edge of the fire and giggled. Probably because I'm circumcised, which makes me look in a state of perpetual sexual excitement to people unaccustomed to the sight of an exposed glans except during lovemaking.

Finally, Warramunga decided the goat was done. He and Cheqchiku set it down on a flat rock and portioned it out to the crowd. Ituru was served first, taking a slice of goat and some stuffing and one of the eggs and more hot sauce. He used a large leaf as a plate and ate with his fingers. To my utter amazement, he spat out the first bite on the ground. Had he lost his mind? We were five days' paddle from anywhere, at the complete mercy of our hosts, and he was spitting out their banquet dish in disgust. I froze, in the act of filling my own leaf, when it happened. The background chatter and laughter stopped too.

Then Ituru laughed aloud and resumed eating, with gusto. The Xixis all laughed. Warramunga laughed, Cheqchiku laughed. Even I laughed. Ituru had played a ceremonial joke.

And so I played one too. I snitched his egg when he wasn't looking. He looked all around for it, but I had put it in my pocket. There was a roar of amusement and, I think, approval when I slipped it secretly back on his leaf and he knocked it, unawares, into the dirt.

The goatmeat was stringy but brilliantly seasoned, as was the mush stuffing. We gorged and, when darkness came, there was dancing to drums around the fire. I joined in as best I could. There seemed to be no special steps or patterns. No one touched, except for some small children who got on each other's shoulders and imitated my height and my awkwardness.

This morning I have a slight hangover, but my mood is good. The Ufas are ready to push off. Good-bye for a while. Best wishes to Mr. Metesky.

Love,
Alan

VI

TOTEMISM TODAY

August 15. The days are calm and I learn to be a frog. War-ramunga devotes spare moments throughout the morning, when we are at work together in the fields, and an hour after lunch, while the village plays, to answering my questions and cramming my head with Xixi lore.

The language is still a problem, but I am trying to minimize the difference between myself and the villagers in other ways. In place of normal clothes, I now wear a penis shield and noth-ing else. At first it chafed and I had trouble tying it on so that it didn't come undone. Thank God that stage is over with.

Since I am, ritually speaking, a boy-child, I am assigned to do boy's work: weeding in the manioc fields and clearing the dung out of the animal pens. It is no accident that the word for dung (aka) and the word for pen (akana) are related.

Warramunga oversees three little boys and me. Since there are no shovels, we pull the goat and tapir shit into piles with small wood scrapers and eventually cart it in a wheelbarrow to the fields. After a few minutes, we are all covered with brown, and I have to be careful not to rub my eyes. My co-workers seem to enjoy their work, but their attention span is short; they break the tedium by throwing turds at each other from time to time. Warramunga stops them, not because he thinks aka is filthy but in order to keep the work on schedule.

He did, however, lose his temper when Wallpa, a nine-year-old brat, hit him by accident with a misaimed tapir pie.

"Asna," he barked. Stinking, noxious. But not filthy. The distinction is important. Warramunga went immediately to the Mashmish and dived into the village swimming hole to wash off. He explained to me that he was contaminated from contact with the tapir manure because he is a tapir (airanpo) and forbidden to touch the clan animal or its excretions. Where other animals or human beings were concerned, he found nothing wrong with touching dung or urine (hisp'a). Indeed, he has made no effort to get me or the other boys to clean up before lunch. They stay reasonably clean by swimming frequently, but brown hands and feet are not infrequent at mealtime, especially since it is almost impossible to keep up a civilized standard of cleanliness without soap, shoes or hard floors.

Although I have resolved not to say much about sanitation these first few weeks, I did object when the rotting entrails of the goat that was killed the night of my arrival were thrown in the river along with the rest of the garbage. Cheqchiku smiled at me and used the word "rimariy," which means "stutter." I gather she was telling me that anyone who could barely express himself had no business telling adults how to run their lives.

"Rimariy," by the way, is interesting for another reason: it illustrates one of the many ways in which the Xixis use reduplication of sounds to express meaning. The verb "to speak" is "rimay." "Rimariy" doubles the "ri" sound and is, therefore, a literal example of stuttering, something like "zézayer" in French, but not exactly. And in Xixi, the reduplication principle encompasses much more. For example, "phuyu" means "cloud," but "phuyu phuyu" refers to a "thick cloud."

The more of this I learn, the less likely they are to dismiss my ideas. And it is clear that they would be much better off if they stopped polluting their source of drinking water and if they washed regularly in boiled water. Every house has someone who is "not feeling well today."

Perhaps the most instructive part of all this, for the moment, however, was Warramunga's upset over the tapir dung. I had thought he was a frog. But it turns out that none of the married men living in frog territory are frogs. They are all tapirs; their children are frogs.

Now that Ituru has left for his own village, I am having great difficulty in asking complicated questions. Nevertheless, after a couple of sessions with the Warramungas, I think I've got the kinship system straightened out. Warramunga couldn't believe that we had nothing like it in the United States so it took a while to make him see how totally ignorant I was of such—to him— basic information.

The system is matrilineal polyandry spread across four exoga- mous clans that intermarry among themselves in a prescribed pattern determined by geographic-totemic moieties, but Kuva, as a village, is endogamous. So much for jargon.

Warramunga explained it more or less this way. The river divides Kuva into an eastern and a western half. Two clans live on the east bank (tapir and piranha); two on the west (frog and jaguar). If you think of the entire village as a circle, which is roughly the way the forest has been cleared, then it makes sense to say that each clan occupies its own quadrant and forms a mini-village within the main settlement. A low-lying line of rocks stretches east-west across the center of Kuva, symbolically dividing northern and southern clans from each other. That is to say, frogs are separated from jaguars by rocks, as are tapirs and piranha, but this separation over land is less important than the division created by the river. Nevertheless, the two axes, stone fence and river, do cut up Kuva into two moieties of overlapping and different meaning. Note that the two water- dwelling totems, frog and piranha, are not combined in either moiety. The two land-dwelling totems, tapir and jaguar, are similarly separate.

Each mini-village has its own characteristic layout. In the

tapir cluster, the houses are arranged in a square around a central fire pit. The piranha houses form a triangle. Frogs live in a hexagon, jaguars in a pentagon. Each clan produces its own food in separate fields and pens at the jungle edge of its quadrant.

Kuva women spend their entire lives in the same clan quadrant. In fact, they often never move out of the house they grew up in. Men, on the other hand, rotate through three clans. Warramunga was born into a tapir household. He was initiated with other tapir adolescents and then spent his bachelor (maqt'a) years in a barracks for unmarried men, in the jaguar quadrant. All tapir men go through the same process. All of them marry frogs and spend their bachelorhood (with other tapirs) among the jaguars. They never have contact with piranhas. I mean they never set foot in the piranha quadrant or speak to a piranha, out of fear. The taboo for tapirs against (animal) tapirs is a taboo of positive feeling. Warramunga explained to me that he did not mean to make me think that he had been disgusted at the tapir dung itself but at his own temerity in putting himself in contact with a revered substance. For piranhas, people and fish, he feels loathing.

Warramunga's sons, of whom I am now one, will follow a path that is the mirror image of their father's. They are born frogs, go through the frog initiation, which Warramunga cannot attend, spend their bachelorhood with the piranhas, where their father cannot visit them (they can visit him, if so inclined, but this is considered bad form), they marry a tapir and live in their wife's mother's house.

This arrangement has several obvious effects on everyday village life. Because of marriage links, the north (tapir-frog) and south (piranha-jaguar) moieties are closely allied. Members of northern clans are always living in the same households, as are members of southern clans. Northerners go south and southerners north only for the brief time of bachelorhood, and even then they live by themselves, seldom entering into the life of the host clan, for they spend most of their time crossing over into the clan quadrant where they will presently marry.

Indeed, the main purpose of the bachelor barracks (avoidance of incest with members of the natal clan is a secondary goal) is to put them within easy reach of an appropriate bride and out of their fathers' control. The logic of the system sees to it that bachelors invariably reside in the quadrant that is taboo for their fathers and just across the rock fence from where the (permitted) girls are.

Now, obviously, it is no great problem for a man who sets his mind to it to cross into the territory of another clan whenever he wants to. Sex between partners of the wrong clans sometimes occurs, but it is dangerous, since, if discovered, it is punished by the expulsion of both parties from their clans. This is a Draconian measure, since it means the end of normal social life for women, who can no longer be spoken to by their female neighbors, and the abrupt severing of life-long ties of camaraderie for men. Both men and women who have been expelled from their clans are, for that reason, also cut off utterly from their mothers. Most important of all, people without a clan have no status in the village. They must scavenge food and live outdoors. Few of them survive more than a year.

Because the punishment is so severe, it is rarely invoked, but it does have a strong deterrent effect on socially aberrant sex.

Normative sex occurs before and after marriage between unmarried men who have gone through initiation and women who have begun to menstruate. They are quite promiscuous during the courtship period. Sexual experimentation is encouraged so long as young tapirs do it with young frogs and young piranhas with young jaguars. Through this process of random gamboling, marriages eventually result (premarital pregnancy is said to be unknown as a result of the universal practice of coitus interruptus, but the existence of a word for abortion ["sulluchiy"—"to cause to abort"] would indicate otherwise, or is abortion reserved for married women?). Generalized social pressure as well as the hardships of bachelor life encourage young men to declare themselves quickly.

The bride has the privilege of saying no, but her decision is less crucial to her than the groom's is to him, for she can marry subsequent husbands and bring them into her house to live with the first. Women with several husbands enjoy great prestige. They also enjoy more active sex lives and more help around the house. But, in practice, it is only the occasional beauty (say, one woman in five) who exercises the right to a second husband during the lifetime of the first. Cheqchiku, with three husbands, is a definite exception, for most men here prefer to marry a woman who has not already married someone else. The first husband enjoys certain unofficial rights after the arrival of the second. But the identity of a child's father is of no official importance, since lineage and clan are both established through the mother.

Even the small amount of polyandry actually practiced in Kuva does, however, have an important effect on curbing population growth. At least 20 percent of the women of childbearing age remain spinsters because there are not enough men to go around. As a result, the population of the village has stayed roughly at the level of 600 for as long as anyone can remember.

Spinsters continue to live in their mothers' houses until they die. If a spinster is the only woman in the house, it reverts to the clan on her death and is given to a married woman sharing the same roof with at least one sister.

This apparently strict, geographically delineated kinship system leaves ample room for personal choice. A bachelor can have his pick of almost any woman over 12 in the clan designated for him. His choice is almost always reciprocated, since the Xixis do not entertain notions of romantic love. And the only restriction that requires the slightest self-restraint is observing the incest taboo against union with one's father's female relatives, namely his mother, her sisters, her daughters and their daughters. That is, grandmothers, great-aunts, aunts and first cousins are out; cousins, nieces and all other women in the right clan are in.

The only unhappy people in the system are the spinsters. But, as Warramunga put it, without them Kuva would be too large for its clearing. The wild game would disappear. And the tribe would not improve over the generations. An outsider might say that while polyandry puts undue pressure on young women to marry and avoid spinsterhood, it helps the Xixis to strike a rough ecological balance with their environment and to practice eugenics informally. The spinsters tend to be stupid, weak or ugly by local standards.

Finally, it may seem that the villages' elaborate clan system would have the effect of cutting people off from each other and of splitting the clans into rival factions. Warramunga argues strenuously that this is not so, that all four clans meet as brothers on the river and in the forest, that even the taboo against speaking to piranhas does not apply to him on neutral ground. There is daily proof of this, he points out, at sundown, when a delegation from each of the four clans paddles out to Kuva's most sacred place, the point where the river and an imaginary extension of the line of the stone fence meet. The paddlers join hands and drop a sacrificial offering into the Mashmish. The offering, I shudder to mention, is garbage.

And therein lies a tale, a tale told to me and the other frog boys by Cheqchiku, who is said to know more myths than any other woman on the west bank.

The Journey to the Stars by Pirogue

Many years ago, a woman was gathering fruit in the top of a tree. Hidden by the foliage, she was able to hear a conversation between two men who had come and sat in the shade of the tree. They were hungry but did not have enough food for two, and so they started to fight. The woman began throwing fruit down to them, hoping to end the dispute, but the fruit changed to stones and killed one of the men. The survivor climbed the tree and dragged the woman down to the ground.

The man's name was Yabarana, and he forced the woman to gather all the rocks she had thrown and bring them with her to his house, where he made her his wife. Often, Yabarana was away for many days at a stretch. He left the woman in the care of a jaguar, who gradually stole all the rocks that had been fruit and hid them in his lair.

One day, when Yabarana returned home, he noticed that the rocks were gone. The woman had guessed where they were and led him to the jaguar's lair. Seeing them approach, the jaguar turned into a worm and crawled into the ground. Yabarana gathered up the rocks and carried them to his pirogue. He and the woman began paddling downstream when a dense fog settled around them. Yabarana, who was paddling in the stern, could not see where to steer. He put his right hand in the water and was bitten by a scorpion. The hand swelled so that he could not paddle. The woman, who was paddling in the bow, knew nothing of this, because the fog was too thick for her to see Yabarana and the wind was howling too loud for her to hear him. So she continued to paddle. Yabarana could do nothing but shout and yelp in pain.

After a time, he saw that this was useless and, besides, he was hungry. He reached forward along the bottom of the pirogue for some food but touched one of the rocks with his swollen hand. The rock changed back to fruit and the hand shrank to its original size. Yabarana then ate the fruit and threw the peel over the side. He reached forward again along the bottom of the pirogue and touched another rock, which also turned back to fruit. In a very short time, Yabarana had eaten all the fruit and thrown all the peels over the side. Meanwhile the woman had continued paddling in the fog. She imagined they were still on the river.

When the fog cleared, she realized that they were moving upward to the sky and that the rocks were all gone. Her husband saw where she had taken them with her paddling and pushed her out of the pirogue. She fell to the ground and a fruit tree grew in the place where she landed. Yabarana continued to paddle across the sky, where he now shines as the sun during the day. At night he descends to the river in his pirogue to hunt and pick fruit. After he finishes his night-long feast, he throws the guts from his meat and the peel from his fruit into the river and climbs the sky once more.

August 17. They warned us about culture shock during training. And I am coming down with a serious case, I think. It isn't any specific part of the routine of life here that is getting me down. I don't mind grubbing in tapir shit or pulling weeds. The people are pleasant, even if they do treat me like a big baby. I deserve that anyway, because in this setting I am an infant. I have none of the skills a nine-year-old should have. I can't spear fish. I don't know what berries to eat or what kinship words are taboo for me.

But the worst part, what nettles and upsets me and leaves me glum and shaky, is that none of the things I *can* do matters at all here. I have no function, no value.

Sure, I could try to teach them English or French, but they don't need foreign languages, and they couldn't understand the vocabulary anyway. How could they make sense out of words like "skyscraper" or "historicism" or "junket"? They have virtually no technology and their language, so far as I can tell at this point, has no way of expressing most abstract ideas.

That's becoming a major problem. For years I have come to expect a certain kind of intellectual conversation. Now those ideas are piling up in my head, swarming to get out. I can almost feel the pressure.

I get up in the morning and I feel like a man from Mars. Nothing I expect to happen happens. I'm not talking here about conscious expectations. Obviously, I anticipate by now that everyone will be practically naked and speak in clicks and squat in the center of the village to shit. I know that every meal or almost every meal will be the same—pounded-manioc gruel. I am even getting used to the idea that Cheqchiku and at least one of her husbands will ball each other three or four feet from my face every night.

It isn't any single new element in my life that catches me unawares, but rather the fact that nothing is the same as before, that I have nothing to reassure me that I am who I am. None of the little details that confirm your identity in America is present here.

Superficially, I have figured this place out as well as I even need to to get through the day. I have more or less mastered the routine, which couldn't be simpler. What I miss is my old routine that kept reinforcing subtly that I was a normal person with a name and a background, not a perplexing anomaly.

I don't want to get out of bed in the morning.

There's an example: get out of bed in the morning. Such a basic idea I can't get it out of my head, even though I no longer have any bed to get out of, since we all sleep on mats.

Language is the most mentally exhausting part of the whole adjustment (am I adjusting or being engulfed?). And the most upsetting, since I didn't expect any trouble with it. It's not learning to put the words together or pronouncing them properly. I'm getting on with that quite well, in fact. The problem is to force what I want to say into a Xixi framework. To think like a Xixi.

Learning other languages was much less draining, because I could settle for technical, superficial proficiency. I could always slip back into my "real" identity any time I wanted to. Here, my real identity is a myth and I am having to construct a new self in order to preserve my sanity.

August 22.   Have reached a point of workable competence in the language. Herewith some observations:

- Xixi has no articles and no prepositions.
- Nouns follow a single declension model; all verbs are conjugated according to the same paradigm.
- All words are accented on the penult except for a few exceptional oxytones. No accents occur further back than the penult.
- Suffixes, particles and postpositions are extremely important.
- Some nouns form complete sentences all by themselves; "wasin": "This is the house."
- Nouns are derived from other nouns by the addition of the suffix "kaq"; "aukana" means "war," "aukanakaq" means "warrior." Nouns of instrumentality are created by the postposition "rurana": "t'anta" means "bread"; "t'anta rurana" is a "bread-making tool."
- Xixi has masculine and feminine gender. M. and F. adjectives are built on entirely different roots: "old" (f.) is "paya"; "old" (m.) is "machu." For animals, the word "orqo" precedes the species name of males; "china" precedes females. E.g., "orqo allqo" is "dog"; "china allqo" is "bitch." The only exception to this is for chicken, where "wallpa" means "hen" and "k'anka" means "cock."
- When a man calls a man "brother," he says "wayqe"; when a woman calls a man "brother," she says "tura." When a man calls a woman "sister," he says "pana"; when a woman calls a woman "sister," she says ñaña.
- All plurals are formed by adding "kuna" at the end of the word.
- "I" ("ñoqa") has two plurals. "Ñoqanchis" means "we," in a sense that includes both the speaker and the person addressed. "Ñoqayku" means "we" in a sense that excludes the person or persons being addressed and includes others not present or at least not being spoken to.
- Xixi has a noun case system identical in structure and function to Latin, in basic details.
- The infinitive ending is "y."

- Basic verbs take on new shades of meaning by incorporating certain particles between the root and the infinitive or ending. E.g., "rimay" means "speak." "Rima-chi-ku-shia-y" means "to cause (chi) oneself (ku) to speak at this moment (shia)." The number of such particles is quite large.

In other words, refined speech in Xixi depends not only on the correct use of noun and verb endings familiar to us already, but also, and especially, on the subtle and expressive use of agglutinative particles. One more example: to disclaim responsibility for a reported statement, one attaches "si" to the verb, or to a noun or adjective. "Warminsi": "She claims to be a woman." "Munasqasi": "He says that he is beloved (but I doubt it)."

August 24.   I gave a short lecture at the fire pit this afternoon about amebiasis, which simple observation tells me nearly everyone in Kuva has a touch of from time to time. That's not surprising. The training manual estimated that, in the tropics, the carrier rate might easily exceed 50 percent.

Well, I've now been all over three of the four clan quadrants in Kuva, and the evidence of amebiasis is right out in the open: runny stools flecked with blood and mucus. Inside the houses, you see the victims, too tired to work, slightly feverish, suffering from slight aches.

Of course, they recover—and then relapse—and recover again. But why should they have to go through life with chronic recurring discomfort, anemia and the constant risk of serious complications like hepatitis and liver abscess? They don't have to use their own shit for fertilizing their crops and vegetable gardens. With the man-hours saved by eradicating the disease, it would be easy to dig latrines. There's plenty of animal manure around to make composting with the garbage practical. And they could still save symbolic amounts of garbage to throw into the river each night. (I don't think they'll ever give up that custom. The sun does have to rise, after all.)

I got the whole frog community together on the pretext of telling them about my native country. And I actually did try to describe American urban civilization to them after a fashion, especially the "wonders of technology" aspect. My plan was to go from there to medical science and then to explain the etiology of amebiasis along with the simple preventive measures.

And so I got up there and told Warramunga and the rest about villages in my country that were 10,000 times the size of Kuva, where the buildings were like 100 of their houses piled on top of each other, and people traveled in wagons that moved by themselves and kept on going all day faster than a man could run.

As I spoke, I looked around at my audience, who were obviously liking my speech but believing not a word. A child asked how it was that the magic wagons could move that fast through the jungle. Cheqchiku shushed the boy, but she did it in such a way that I knew she didn't believe me either. And why should she? I'm at the point where I barely believe in those memories myself. The frogs are right. It doesn't make sense to put up buildings that high or drive that fast. To the people of Kuva it sounded as if I were boasting about my own tribe, in a ridiculously obvious way, in order to build myself up in their eyes.

Well, it's true, isn't it? Even I don't think skyscrapers are important human achievements. As artifacts, they *are* essentially boastful.

At any rate, I changed tacks and talked about our great doctors, shamans of large wisdom, who had taught me a simple way to keep from being sick ("onqo") all the time the way Sinchi was (I pointed to the amebic sufferer of the moment). His mother immediately challenged me to cure the boy.

So I had to explain that I couldn't cure but could only prevent the disease. Everyone nodded patronizingly.

By this time, I was wishing I had kept my mouth shut. But there was nothing else to do but finish. I picked up my Peace

Corps trench shovel, which the crowd greatly admired, and dug a latrine. I shoveled a few stray turds into it. That made no impression whatever. Clearly, realism was essential. I crouched over the pit and showed them what it was for. Thoroughness obliged me to make both number 1 and number 2, and the situation made that part of the lecture very easy. Having wiped myself with a banyan leaf from overhead and then dropped the leaf into the hole, I filled the latrine with dirt and walked to the river, where I washed my hands in a bowl before an audience of at least 400.

This morning I came down with a spectacular case of dysentery and have been thanking heaven all day that there is no distant latrine off in the woods to run to. You couldn't make me walk to the river to wash. *Entamoeba hystolytica* wins the match in straight sets.

August 25.   Cheqchiku took pity on me. First, she gave me Ipecac (at last a cognate!) and that made me vomit up an awful green stream. Then she told me a story, as is her wont.

The Origin of Medicine

Once upon a time, in the days before people lived in proper houses and villages, a man who had just ceased to be a boy was hunting flamingo in a great marsh in the foothills of the Tumuc-Humac. He had been hunting for many days and used all his arrows. His food had run out and his blowgun felt heavy on his shoulder.

A tapir saw him and changed herself into a beautiful young woman with small, high breasts. She emerged from a thicket at the edge of the marsh and invited the young man to follow her home to dinner. This was a welcome offer. The young man had been filling his stomach with nothing but wet vetch for two days and his stomach felt sour.

The tapir's lair was nearby in a glade of ranunculus. Soon the young man had gorged on smoked cayman tail and corn beer. He felt drowsy and lay down by the fire. The tapir-woman lay down beside him and pressed close to him for warmth. After the young man had fallen asleep and was snoring, she removed his penis shield and made his organ stiff by rubbing it with honey.

This awakened the young man, but he pretended to be still asleep and continued to snore, while keeping one eye half-open. The tapir-woman finished her massage, rolled the man gently on his back and mounted him. He lay motionless, while she moved her vagina up and down over his penis.

But just at the moment of orgasm for the man, the woman stopped moving and rolled to one side, still holding the man's penis in her vagina, which was very small and tight. The man cried out in pain—the tapir-woman was stretching his penis to enormous length—and tried to escape. Though he struggled with all his strength, however, he was unsuccessful and his penis had meanwhile stretched to the length of a paddle.

In desperation, he told the tapir-woman a story about Rosqo (the hornbill), who was so greedy for honey that he stuck his beak into an active hive and ended up with the swollen face that he still carries around with him today.

Tapir-woman laughed so hard she loosened her grip on the man. He escaped to the middle of the marsh, where the tapir could not follow, dragging his long penis in the water to soothe it.

The next morning, two otters swam by and took pity on the poor man. They chewed the roots of the kloqsi *(Myrrhaena kleinii)* and brought back its juice in their mouths. By spreading it on the misshapen organ with their tongues, they shrank the man's penis back to its original size.

This took several days. During that time, while one otter would apply the herbal poultice, the other discussed the man's childhood with him. (The otters had been friends of the man's father.) They persuaded him to forgive the old man, even though he had ridiculed his son and driven him away years before. All fathers and sons fight, one of the otters said, but it is also natural for them to make peace with one another and for the son to return and care for his aged parent once he has proved himself in the hunt and with women.

On the day that the young man felt well enough to walk again and travel, he sighted a flamingo and felled it with his first arrow. He and the otters feasted. Then the man said good-bye and took the feathers to his father, who used them to make a roof on the house they built together before the rainy season began.

September 6.   Have concluded the only way to make Kuva conscious that onqo comes from the indiscriminate use and disposal of aka* is to prove it to them by taking on the job of sanitation and composting myself. I have told each household that I will pick up their garbage and nightsoil, and they seem to be willing to go along with the project, or at least too polite to oppose the chief's crazy paleface adopted son.

It took most of the day to dig a pit six by six by six with my trench shovel. Suri, the girl from the tapir quadrant, helped me move dirt. And between the two of us—she is quite sturdy—we produced a fairly dramatic latrine at the edge of the forest. Suri jumped into it with her jaguar-fang necklace flying. I hadn't noticed until then, but she is quite poqo.

A crowd of people came to gawk and kusichay me on digging such a big hole in the ground, the biggest they've ever seen. And I really thought I had a triumph on my hands when one old woman actually crouched over the edge.

She was putting me on, however, and had no intention of using the latrine. It was a start, though. Everything special here begins with a put-on. It seems to be the Xixi way of relieving anxiety when they have to face a new and disruptive event. And life is so traditional and devoid of surprises normally that a

---

*See Xixi glossary, page 211.

latrine does pose a real threat to the natural order as they know it.

I am, I now see, a constant source of anxiety to my neighbors in the frog quadrant, because I am an outsider with new ideas that threaten nature and custom, which they revere in the highest degree.

The best way to quiet their fears is to borrow their own favorite ploy and put them on. I did just that on the way back from the latrine. As we all passed the old woman's house, I nonchalantly squatted in front of her door—but left no trace. Everyone laughed and it was all very good P.R. for my project. We'll see how much good it did, though, tomorrow, when I start my first pickups.

September 10

Dear Missy,

This is the first opportunity I've had to write you since I got here. A canoe is leaving for the trading post at Gé tomorrow morning, to barter jaguar pelts for kitchen matches and salt. The trip back and forth takes ten days, but it is the only way to communicate with the outside.

If this letter seems disjointed, there are reasons. I am having great difficulty in setting down what has happened to me over the last month. English doesn't have any of the right overtones. I could, for instance, tell you about my official work, my latrine project, which involves shoveling shit and burying it. The village tolerates me, but I have to do all the work, and it is too early for any results to show. Dysentery is still endemic. Even I am beginning to doubt if Western medical science is right about the connection between nightsoil and amebiasis.

You begin to doubt many things out here. So much just doesn't apply. The old words shrivel in your mouth. It struck me the other day that I'm living in a true socialist community. The means of production—fields, animal pens, the river and forest —are held in common. Everyone shares the produce equally.

Hunters divide their catch among the members of their clan. Even houses don't really belong to anyone. They revert to the clan if a family produces no female issue. No one owns anything larger than a hand tool, and even then there's no question in my mind that the clan effectively "owns" the canoe builder's chisels and the women's bone needles. The products of these tools, anyway—the canoes and clothing—are all shared.

So this is socialism. But it means nothing to say that. Socialism is a reaction against inequalities of ownership and wealth. It implies some kind of redistribution. The Xixis don't even have a word for ownership or property. When they talk about robbery, they mean plunder, taking something from an enemy village.

But they still don't conceive of plunder as a violation of any abstract principle of ownership. Looting is an extension of battle. It rights a wrong and re-establishes the natural order. Stealing an enemy village's goat, at least as the Xixis see it, is an act of revenge, not an unlawful transaction.

Warramunga, the chief of Kuva and my churichaq, my adoptive father, laughs when I ask him about such things. He thinks it's funny that I am always trying to use words as abstractions, "pull them away from life." His language, I almost said our language, has no legitimate abstract words. "Sumay" means something like "honor," I suppose, but its usage is not highflown in the way our word is. "Sumay" really applies to someone who is well known in the village—outside his clan—for some specific accomplishment such as dancing well or shooting an arrow accurately. Truth (cheqa) is not a concept here; it is the opposite of lie, not of falsehood.

The language (the word for "language" is really the infinitive of the verb "to speak") is, however, lavishly supplied with specific vocabulary. "Phuyurqoy" means: "The sky is unexpectedly clouding over." "Eqo" is a child conceived while the mother was still suckling a previous child. "Hanpina" is a disease that should be treated with medicine, as opposed to one that will not yield to medication.

"Much'a" means "kiss." And, picturesquely, "much'u" refers to the nape of the neck. But, best of all, "much'apayay" means to kiss over and over again.

And that makes me think of you and what it would be like if I were still in your world and not committed to martyrdom in shit at the edge of the world's largest rain forest. I can't picture it. We have lost the video portion of our program down here. Sometimes I can hear your voice, but my memory of your face gets hazier and hazier. Please don't think that means I am forgetting *you*. No, I want you more than ever and cling to the prospect of your visit like a sloth to a mahogany branch. You will, you must, meet me in Gé on December 20, as we promised each other.

Until then,

Much'a much'a

Alan

September 15.   The compost heap is turning out well, heating up from bacterial action according to Hoyle, I mean Rodale. My fellow frogs have stopped making assikuna whenever they pass it. Even in Kuva, I guess, traditions can be invented overnight. And when they see what my fertilizer does for their manioc production, they'll stop calling me Mitma. I'll be a myth in my own time: Once upon a time, a stranger came to Warramunga's manioc fields. His skin was pale and hair grew all over him for he had changed himself from a monkey into a man, which was obvious from the way he stuttered when he spoke. He was very lazy, would not hunt and would not fish and knew no good stories. All day long he played with aka and gathered garbage from whoever would give him some.

One day, Warramunga followed him to see what he was doing with all the garbage and tapir moonpies. Mitma dragged his smelly load out back near the edge of the great forest and threw it carefully on a pile that was already as big as the boulder of the sun. To Warramunga the pile looked as if it were smoking. He waited until Mitma had left and then went up to the pile with the wary step of the hunter of toucans. He touched the pile and it was warm and steaming and it spoke to Warramunga in the language of birds: "Protect and favor Mitma, for he will bring you great bounty. He is a famous sorcerer in his own country; I am his slave."

The next day, Mitma buried the pile under the ground. Warramunga was sad; he expected miracles but now the pile was gone, interred like a fallen warrior. But on the first night of the next full moon, Mitma led Warramunga back to the place where the pile was buried. And there was manioc there, as tall as Mitma himself. Warramunga turned around to congratulate the hairy visitor but he had reverted to his monkey form and swung off into the heart of the forest on a dangling liana.

I wonder if Missy will really visit me here. Does it make sense? I suppose she could sleep in Warramunga's house.

On second thought, I can't imagine it at all, Missy on a dank mat in a thatched hut full of lice and naked Xixis, trying to sleep while Cheqchiku takes on all three husbands.

September 17.   Suri has been helping me pick up garbage nearly every afternoon for the past week. Can she possibly have invented a new kind of flirtation? I hadn't thought about it before, but for her I am an eligible beau. I'm a frog; she's a tapir. We're both marriageable. And after the initiation ceremony this fall . . .

If you took any of this seriously, you could also mention that the frogs will send only one new bachelor across to the piranha barracks this year, besides me, that is. And Khramuphu is no prize. He has yaws, which doesn't help his complexion and makes him limp around because of the ulcerative lesions on the soles of his feet.

And since you mention all of that, you may as well admit that I am as horny as a ram. I caught myself looking at Suri bending over to pick up garbage this afternoon. Thirteen years old and just skipped across the barrier into womanhood, firm and downy and a good pair of ñuñus.

Cut it out, Mitma. You can't start lusting after little Suri. You are a representative of the Corps de la Paix with a serious mission. Two missions, in fact. Which reminds me that I haven't looked at my radiation-warning device lately, haven't even worn it for a week, but for Christ's sake it is a pain to have to carry the thing around inside a penis shield. There's nothing to clip it to; so when it isn't chafing, it falls out, usually into a tapir brick.

I just can't wait until the fucking Pentagon—or whoever—tries to start a uranium mine out here. The termites alone should make that a picnic. A team of them consumed the packing crate that held my superspook shortwave radio. I don't know exactly when it happened, because, not needing to send frequent code bulletins to Interpol yet, I had left it in the back of the house, still packed. Well, with the crate gone, the humidity got to it. The damn thing is rusted tight as a macaw's asshole and probably short-circuited too. (Luckily, my books are in a metal trunk.) So now, in case of emergency (Russian agents exfoliate the jungle and start airlifting out fissionable ore in Ilyushins), I have nothing to do but signal for the Batmobile. Oops, nowhere to plug in the Bat beacon. Better to send a message to Aquaman in a bottle. Do the Mashmish piranhas cooperate with him? And where will I find a bottle around here? Clearly, I'm trapped. While I'm sitting here scooping poop, the Chicoms are shipping out the U–235 inside souvenir blowguns. Yes, velly heavy. Fine mahogany browgun.

Mao builds a cheap nuclear deterrent, destroys every Western country (except Albania) with a pre-emptive strike carried in millions of time-fused fortune cookies. Meanwhile, I, the last living American, know nothing about it. "We never hear about anything important in Kuva, my deah." And in June of 1965, I paddle downstream in what's left of my city clothes to discover a race of three-eared mutants running the world.

Fortunately, I have a refuge, a place where even strontium 90 doesn't dare fall out. Kuva. I tie on my trusty penis shield (packed a few days before so that I could show it to my parents: "But, Ma, all the other guys wear them") and paddle back upriver, looted Polaroids steamy at the sudden realization that the Xixis are the last hope for the survival of the human race as we know it. What's more, given five or ten years, I can cure them of elephantiasis. All we have to do is build a screened dome around the entire village. Sorry, each clan can have its own dome. Where will the screen come from? We'll build our own factory. "The Peace Corps stands squarely behind the development of new projects in the field, especially those that bring economic viability to remote and poor areas. Cottage industries work especially well."

You are giddy, Mitma.

September 22.   The mail is here from Gé. Wet but legible.

                                                     September 5

Dear Alan,

Your father and I are spending Labor Day weekend here in Mackinac missing our wonderful boy very much. You should really write us just once in a while. Now that we can't call on Sundays, the mail is very important. And don't think that because you're part of the international set and halfway round the world, you aren't still our son and don't owe a lot of your fine qualities to the home you grew up in.

Did the packages arrive? Your grandmother sent you something too and would like to hear from you. It would mean so much to her.

The McQuilkins are here with us, which is nice. We have gone on some lovely walks on this magic island. No cars are permitted. We feel so close to nature. You must feel the same way where you are.

Daddy and I would like to send you a tape recorder for your

birthday so that you could exchange tapes with us. Mary Barton gets tapes all the time from Sue, who is teaching English for the Peace Corps in Istanbul. It must be awful there. You are much better off being away from a big city.

Have you made friends with any of the natives? I hope you won't cut yourself off from that experience and just "hobnob" with the other volunteers. Still, you know how pleased Daddy and I would be if you brought a pretty "volunteer" home for Christmas. I'm sure the Peace Corps wouldn't say no to that.

Write soon.

Love and kisses,

Mom & Dad

September 8

To: Casper

From: Kaufman

We have no illusions in these quarters about how tough what you are going through must be. The official speculation in Washington is that you are dead, in case you are interested. And that doesn't seem to have created great sadness in the Oval Office, where, as you are certainly aware, your name is unmentionable. Sometimes, in fact, I wonder whether or not your assignment was made up in order to put you in cold storage.

Don't feel guilty if you don't have much progress to report as of now. Should you simply survive the first year without losing your mind, that will beat the world's record for living alone with the Xixis. Even Ituru couldn't stand it. He drifted back through here last week looking for work.

I really don't have much else to say. No advice or anything. But you could do me a great favor by sending a flash by SW if you get wind of any cocaine traffic in your neck of the woods. It would be a feather in my cap if I could help the T-men make a bust. Washington is very interested.

Thanks and Regards,

K.

September 12

Dear Alan,

Metesky is a beast and I have left him. He wanted a cook and a slave, not a woman. But what could you expect from a man with two pairs of golf shoes? I am ashamed to admit that I polished them for him once.

Well, that should make you happy. And you also might be pleased to know that your adoring little friend got an A— in organic and was told by Dean Ruhrschmid, whom she ran into in Brigham's, that she was a cinch to get into Harvard Med. So don't worry about any tropical diseases you may pick up out there. I will be able to cure them when you get back.

"What is she doing now?" you are asking yourself, having gloated fully over my debacle with the mad bomber's cousin. (How restrained of you not to point out the similarity in names. *He* did it wherever we went.) Well, I am back in my old apartment all alone, jerking off with the latest issue of *Muscle Man.*

Don't you wish. In fact, I am sitting all alone in my old apartment wishing you were here, even though you are the most egotistical, cold, selfish son of a bitch yet thrown up by the evolutionary process.

Also, I am reading the literature on jungles, from Conrad to Céline. Graham Greene's *Journey Without Maps* is very good, but Gide is better. *Le Voyage au Congo* is probably the best piece of personal journalism ever written. (You must have read it, but here goes.) The style, it goes without saying, is the most natural, mature first person achieved in our time. So it is a successful "personal" book, no? Like the rest of the Journals. What you don't expect—he didn't expect it either, which is in a way the best part—is the reportage. Without even meaning to, he begins uncovering horrendous evidence of colonial exploitation by a French company in Central Africa. Then he publishes the book and, because Gide is Gide, it provokes a

137

national scandal in France. The head of the fascist company loses his job. And they all live happily ever after, except that Gide liked boys.

And so do I. Do you still want me to visit over Christmas? I will almost be a Radcliffe graduate by then, 21 years old, and willing to endure any hardship to stay with you. Extreme heat and filth will not faze me. I will boil your shirts. I have read Maugham and know what to do in the bush.

But you must already have found yourself a willowy half-caste with almond eyes. Her name is Yolanda, and I am sunk. Say it isn't so.

Love,
Missy

October 9.   Spread compost in the manioc field today. Suri helped. Fingers crossed hoping for a bumper crop.

October 11.   Warramunga took me hunting for jaguars yesterday. I carried the arrows and the curare. He had warned me not to whack off the night before; so I felt full of vim and vital fluids as we set out into the jungle at dawn.

He led the way. I should say his scraggly little yellow dog led the way, racing ahead through the trees—you forget how large they are after a while (can't see the trees for the forest?)—following some scent or other, yipping constantly.

Warramunga is not usually what you would call loquacious. And as a hunter he is virtually mute. Early on in the expedition, I asked him how the plans for the initiation were coming along, just to make small talk. He stopped very dramatically, looked at me very hard and told me not to ask questions. "OK, chief," I thought and slogged on.

The bugs stopped after we had gone a half-mile or so into the jungle. We were making good progress on a barely visible old path that moved upward gradually and away from the river. It was very noisy from monkey traffic overhead and birds. Warramunga stopped to listen every few hundred yards, cocking one ear up and scratching his stippled cheeks pensively.

"I'm listening for the jaguar," he explained. I listened too and even managed to pick out a familiar bird call or two. But no jaguar. Do they do a bass purr? I wondered. Well, Warramunga didn't hear one either.

Then the path stopped. We kept on moving upcountry, but slower now, pushing our way through tangled vegetation. Warramunga looked back at me from time to time to see how I was making out. I got the impression he was testing me.

After a while—it must have been around 10:30—we stopped to eat cassava bread. "The jaguar is near," Warramunga said. "Listen to the forest." I listened. Very hard. I heard no jaguar sounds, no thundering meows, no indications of a large beast crashing through the bush in pursuit of prey, no death rattles from small game. In fact, compared to earlier in the day, it was quiet.

And that was the point. "He has frightened them all away, Mitma," Warramunga said. "You can smell the panic-shit all around us. Look at allqo."

The dog was huddled in a ball under a mahogany knee. Some hound.

A small fat furry animal waddled by us a few yards away. It looked something like a prairie dog. Without any preliminary warning, Warramunga leaped on it, like the jaws of a trap snapping down. He came back to where I was standing, holding the little creature by the scruff of the neck. It squealed much louder than you would have guessed, gnashed its stubby teeth and urinated from fury on Warramunga's knee. He poked it, hard, in the ribs. More squealing and gnashing.

"Get a vine of your height, O Mitma," he said softly while bashing the animal against a tree to quiet it. "We must make a noose."

There was more squealing and more bashing, while I pulled down a liana, cut it to size against a sharp rock and tied a hangman's knot. Warramunga motioned me toward him. The animal had begun to shiver. I dropped the noose over its head and gave the loose end of the liana to Warramunga, who pulled the knot tight enough so that it wouldn't slip off. Then he handed me the animal, which lurched out of my grip before I could get the knack of controlling him. Warramunga pulled the vine taut, but the animal was essentially free now at the end of a five-foot tether. He was fighting for his life, scurrying back and forth, snapping at our toes.

I picked up a fallen branch to use as a club. "Do not kill the beast, my young friend," Warramunga called out. "You must assail him with your hand, as I did, from behind."

Warramunga, I thought, was laying on the chiefly rhetoric a bit thick, considering that, at the moment he gave me those grandly styled directions, he was skipping back and forth across the clearing followed closely by a crazed and vicious agouti.

For some reason, just then, I remembered the name of the animal from a color plate in an edition of *The Swiss Family Robinson.* But hadn't that agouti been passive and cuddly? The question would have to be resolved later on.

I dived at the agouti. And missed. Dived again. Missed again. The third dive got him. I yanked on the noose line and only then noticed that my wrist was bleeding, from the top side, out of four little teeth marks.

Warramunga threw the end of the vine over a branch and pulled. I let go and he suspended the agouti just off the ground, securing the line in place with another knot.

My wrist, the right one, ached, but the bleeding had already stopped; so I said nothing to Warramunga, who smiled, winked at me in actual fact, and carried his blowgun into the jungle to a place about 20 feet from the still squirming agouti. I followed with the dog at my heels.

We waited silently for at least an hour. Warramunga held the blowgun ready and twisted a poison dart around in his teeth like a cigar. My wrist throbbed. "And I chose this instead of graduate school," I thought.

The agouti screamed and Warramunga aimed the blowgun. A jaguar, no, a pair of jaguars, bounded into the clearing and began to tear the agouti apart with their fangs. One suddenly fell to the ground. I felt Warramunga nudge me. He wanted another arrow. I fumbled for it, dipped it in the curare and passed it to him. By this time the other jaguar had smelled us and was coming our way. Warramunga shot the dart, threw down his blowgun and started to run away. The jaguar was too close and he raced to climb a tree.

This all took only seconds, but they were crucial seconds. I had stood there, mesmerized. A flash of spotted fur broke the spell. I looked around for a weapon and found a loose branch. The jaguar lunged at Warramunga, who was running in my direction.

I swung the branch down as hard as I could on the jaguar's head, but the force of his leap carried him onto Warramunga, who collapsed under the weight.

I fainted.

The next thing I remember, as they say in the movies, was seeing Warramunga skin the second jaguar. He had already finished the first one and spread out the pelt to dry.

"So you have finished your nap. It was a sleep well earned, Mitma."

The poison must have taken effect while the jaguar was in mid-air. But I certainly wasn't going to insist on that point. It isn't every day that a young linguist gets credit for clubbing a jaguar to death. Or helping to kill it. Hadn't Warramunga found the arrow? Maybe it had fallen out. I just couldn't have really dispatched the beast with one blow. By now the cleaning and skinning of the animal had gone too far to be sure if an arrow had pierced the flesh.

"Mitma, I truly thought I was dead when he fell on me. His weight crushed the breath from my lungs."

Warramunga cut the heart of the jaguar out of the bloody cavity and handed it to me.

"I ate the first one. This is yours. The magic is not powerful unless the heart is still warm."

I took the heart. It was the size of a fist and certainly warm enough to eat.

I gagged. Warramunga looked puzzled. I calculated at least five big mouthfuls. I closed my eyes and tried to remember the endings for the first declension in Latin. One bite and a quick gulp. Puella. Two bites. Puellae. Three. Puellae. Four. Puellam. Five. Puella with a long *a*.

"Now you are kututu, Mitma. Does it not feel good?"

"Yes, Warramunga. Thank you."

"We have done well in this hunting today. Cheqchiku will be proud of us."

He finished cleaning the second jaguar and spread the skin out carefully. The flayed carcasses and viscera lay in a red heap nearby, dotted with flies.

"Do you ever resent living in her house?" I asked.

"Why should I not like living with my wife? She is a good wife. Two others chose her."

"Doesn't that make you jealous?"

"No. We share her equally."

"But you are chief."

"My penis is the same as other men's." He pulled it out to show me.

"In my country," I explained, "a man, especially a chief, would insist on having his wife to himself every night."

"Your chiefs must not be very busy if they can spend every night making love. It is foolish to waste so much energy on sex."

"Perhaps. But they also want to be sure that their wives bear their children."

"Their children? Children belong to the wife's clan. They come from her womb, don't they?"

"Yes, but from the man's seed too."

"If the seed is kututu, it will show in the child's face. Otherwise, the child is not worth claiming."

"Don't two husbands of the same wife ever dispute the fatherhood of a child?"

"They have more important things to do. And so do we."

He handed me one of the skins, and we started walking back to the village. Flies buzzed around the skins, but the path was downhill now and Warramunga strode quickly. He was jubilant over the hunt and shared his pouch of coca leaves with me. Soon my wrist stopped aching and the weight of the pelt seemed to lift from my shoulders. The drug also lightened Warramunga's tongue, and he told me a story.

Warramunga's Story

Before the great flood that destroyed the first race of men, seven brothers lived with Malkatuna where two rivers met. She cooked for them and cleaned the hut. She kept the fire burning and decided disputes among them. In return, they hunted for food. They brought her red clay which she used to paint her body.

During a great wind, the bees who lived in a hive in an old hollow tree next to Malkatuna's hut could not find the strength to fly home. Instead, they were swept into the deep place where the rivers joined. They drowned.

The brothers saw, when the wind stopped howling and returned to the sky, that the hive no longer buzzed. The eldest brother reached into the hollow tree and his hand stuck on the honeycomb. The others pulled him loose and discovered honey on his hand. This was the first time that any of them had seen honey or tasted its sweetness, which the eldest brother noticed when he tried to lick his hand clean.

The brothers agreed among themselves not to disturb the hive for fear of angering the bees. But, secretly, each of them, except the eldest, later cut away a piece of the comb, ate half of it and gave the rest to Malkatuna, who consumed her sweet gifts and said nothing about them.

Soon she became obviously pregnant, despite the fact that she swallowed pebbles from the river and slept on nettles. For nine months, she did not menstruate. Her belly swelled. And the brothers fell to quarreling among themselves. Each accused the other of seducing Malkatuna. To settle the argument, they threatened her with torture if she did not reveal which one of them her lover was.

Malkatuna insisted on her innocence, but when this only angered the brothers more, she said that Jaguar had raped her while they had all been hunting. The brothers left to revenge themselves and pursued Jaguar for many days, without success, for Malkatuna had warned the beast of his danger. He turned himself into a flamingo for safety and passed his time wading at the river's edge. His urine brought the bees back to life. They returned to their hollow tree and rebuilt the hive.

It was the full moon the night the brothers finally returned to the hut, hungry and wet. Malkatuna greeted them and gave birth to a son through her mouth. The eldest brother looked at the baby boy's face and recognized the features of his brothers there, the nostrils of one, the ears of another, and so on. He concealed his anger, however, and went out in the darkness, saying that he had to urinate. Actually, he had decided to rob the hive of its honey and then go away, leaving his brothers and Malkatuna to endure the revenge of the bees when they returned.

The moon lit his way to the hollow tree, where the bees lay sleeping. But when he put his hand in to take the honey, he awakened them. They swarmed over him and stung him so that his body swelled and burst. Jaguar, changed back to his old shape, drank up the blood and devoured the body, except for the eyes, which a pitying moon brought to live with her in the sky.

October 12. "From high to low . . ." This morning, all achy from the hunt, I went to look for a book in the corner of the house where I store my things, thinking I would take the day off with *Hydriotaphia*. The trunk was empty.

No Thomas Browne, no Shakespeare, no Pléiade *Comédie Humaine*, no Proust. *Clarissa* gone, Gibbon gone, Simenon and Dante, Angela Thirkell, James, *Bouvard et Pécuchet*, Kuryłowicz on ablaut, Musil, Kraus, Dryden, Catullus, Homer, Theocritus, the *Tractatus*, Longfellow (brought for comic relief) and Auden. All gone.

Suri would know what happened. Where was she? Why hadn't she been there last night when we got back with the skins? Practically the whole village came over to admire them.

I hurried outside. Paddled across to the tapir quadrant. No Suri. Paddled back to the frog village and eventually worked my way back to the compost heap. Suri was piling garbage for a new batch. She was concentrating very hard on her work, said hello without looking up.

Guilty knowledge? I stopped for a second as I realized there was no way to ask her directly about what had happened. Xixi has no word for "book."

I settled on "Suri, someone took the things out of my silver box. Do you know where the things are now?"

Looking at her again, more closely this time, I saw that she was crying. She stood up and led me to the latrine and pointed down. My cache of advanced Western culture lay half-buried under moist tapir dung. Another Xixi put-on.

To them, it *was* a good joke. How could you blame illiterates for abusing books? There was no point in mounting an investigation or losing my temper. The only thing to do was what I did —jump into the pit and toss the books out.

I sank to my hips in warm manure and European prose. The smell was almost unbearable. Remember that the temperature in Kuva is always around 90 and that my library had been steeping in decomposing shit for twenty-four hours.

Right at waist level, I found the eight volumes of Balzac, rice-paper pages glued together. Homer was under my right foot, humiliated but still legible. Shakespeare almost got left in the latrine he was so thoroughly covered with brown.

It took an hour. Then we spent the rest of the day wiping the books clean. By the end, I was covered from head to toe. And there was only one place for us to wash. The Mashmish, the river I had been sent to clean up. We walked downstream of the village along the bank to a place where I thought no one would see us and dived in. Suri, who needed a bath almost as much as I did, followed.

It was a scene from the life of Gauguin now. The filth rinsed away and left the white exile alone in a clear river with his bare-breasted brown nymph, splashing under the tall trees with lush gold and green exotic plants fluttering. A drum beat softly in the distance.

"What are they?" Suri asked.

"Books," I said, coining my first Xixi word. "They contain the myths of my people."

She looked puzzled. I pulled her up onto the bank and taught her the alphabet by scraping letters in the dirt with a stick and making the appropriate noises. She caught on immediately; so I moved on to making complete words, my favorite Xixi words: "pachamama," "phallallallay," "qaqya," "qhotototoy." She tried simpler ones: her name, "sawa," "t'ankana," "khuyay." Continuing the game, I scratched out the letters for "cheq-chikachay." She saw what I meant and, blushing, dived back into the Mashmish and swam home against the current. Literacy has its benefits even in a society without a written literature.

Where was it all leading? I wondered on the way back to the frog village. An affair with Suri? The idea made no sense, unless I was prepared to be completely cynical about her. She wanted me forever, I was quite sure. How could I make her understand that I was only staying for two years and then going back to America? She would probably want to go with me, but even if I taught her English . . .

Cheqchiku greeted me with a loud cry of welcome, pulled me with her into the hut and then disappeared outside. Warramunga sat in the stuffy obscurity of the hut, smoking a long pipe, which he used to motion for me to sit down across from him.

"It is almost time for you to go," he uttered solemnly. "I am sorry and joyful, both."

"Have I done something wrong? Why must I leave you?"

"Every son leaves his father. You are ch'apu; you have been kututu in the hunting of jaguar. It is time to go away to the mountains."

He was sending me to be initiated.

"No, Warramunga. It is not right for me to go. I am not a real Xixi. I have been in your house for only a few weeks, and some day not too far off I will return to my own people."

"You are my adopted son. The frogs have too few sons. If we send only the boy who limps, the mountains will think we are mocking them and cause floods. The tapirs need husbands for their women. You must not insult us by refusing. Do not dishonor yourself with mancha."

"I am sorry."

"You must accept or leave Kuva. No clan will feed you if you fail to face the mountains bravely. I would have to drive you from my house."

"I would not want that, Warramunga. I have been happy here."

"Then you agree to go to the mountains?"

I nodded, feeling as if, for the first time in Kuva, I was in real danger. Not physical danger. The initiation for frogs was short and did not involve facial tattooing or any risk of death. Rather, I was afraid of losing myself in the ritual, of shuffling off that inner certainty that I was not a Xixi. I have been clinging to my own identity with less and less strength as the weeks had passed.

You will doubt that I could feel threatened by the prospect of a week in the mountains devoted to the pursuit of animism.

I can only reply that you have not felt yourself gradually sinking away out of one self into another. You have not let a new language invade your thoughts like an incubus, parasitize your mind until the words and memories of your earlier life spoke to you as from another room, muffled voices from a dream.

Three months ago, I would have joined you in doubting these fears, but now, when I am beginning to feel the need for an English dictionary to continue this diary, when I can no longer remember, except in dreams, the way my old friends looked, when letters from the other world barely connect me again with my old life, now I am worried and fearful of going further along the path I have taken.

Leave, then, you will say. Paddle back to Gé. Get out. Save yourself by returning immediately to civilization. No one will blame you for failing in Kuva where everyone has failed.

That's not entirely true, you know. A failure is a failure, no matter how justifiable. And think of how silly my justification will sound in Chiotteville. I'll have to tell them I left my post because I was afraid to go through the same initiation procedure that every Xixi adolescent submits to. Or I could make something up. Tell them the village was taken over by marauders from another village who shrank everyone's head but mine.

That might work. But, anyway, pleasing the Peace Corps isn't my problem. I have to please myself. My civilized half doesn't want to go back to civilization yet. My Xixi half, which gets stronger every day, is pushing me to go through the initiation, to prove myself, become a man and find out what the big mystery is.

Well, I have two weeks to decide.

October 20.   Suri decided there was no point in continuing to write Xixi. No one else but me can read it, and there's nothing to read *in* it. So she's started nagging me to teach her English. She is very quick and, thanks to her illiterate's memory, she forgets nothing. I wish English spelling were more logical. It's embarrassing having to teach it to someone.

I need to find her something to read. My books are not really suitable, I don't think. Probably, I should write some stories for her, things that aren't full of references to snow and God and chastity and automobiles, etc.

October 28

A Story for Suri

A young woman lived with her family in a place with no trees. Years before she was born, the people of her tribe had cut down all the trees near them in order to build houses. The houses were very grand and strong, but there were no birds and the sun beat straight down on the village.

Since the young woman had never seen any trees or heard birds or napped under a tree, she did not miss any of those things. She was happy enough at home, sewing and cooking and waiting for a husband to come and take her to his house. (In her village, wives went to live with their husbands and sometimes did not get a chance to visit their mothers for days at a time.)

One afternoon, she was reading a book in front of her house. She wore a white dress, a sort of cloth robe that covered her from neck to knees. That was the normal costume for women in her country. The sun was beating down as usual and the book was not amusing; so the young woman put it down and was about to go inside to help with dinner. Then, a strange man appeared, a man from a distant place who did not speak her language.

He made a sign to show that he was hungry. The young woman invited him in for a snack. Her mother cried, for she had guessed immediately what would happen. The man stayed in the house until he had learned the local language. Then, he seduced the young woman. She wanted to marry him, and he agreed.

But one morning just before the wedding was to have taken place, the man turned into a dewdrop and was drunk by the sun, who spat him back on the country he came from during a rainstorm. He turned into a mountain pool. The young woman cried and tore her white dress from sadness. Her tears fell to the hot earth and sank belowground into the soil. Eventually they trickled into an underground stream that flowed, unseen by the world, to the faraway country of the vanished young man. There they joined him. Her tears and his droplets flowed together, and at the exact place where they merged, a white water lily grew and still grows today.

October 31.   Initiation begins tomorrow. I have decided to go because I cannot persuade myself that there is any advantage, any overwhelming advantage at any rate, to escape. If my civilized half is worth holding on to, it will survive a Xixi initiation. If not, the hell with it.

_____* Warramunga's shout woke me the first morning. I had not slept well because of apprehension. And so I was out of the house in seconds when the chief cried out in alarm. It all must have been staged, but well staged. A man in a warty frog mask had pushed Warramunga to the ground. I went to help him get up, but the stranger grabbed me and tied my hands together tightly behind my back with a piece of liana. He shoved me along to the river bank, where Khramuphu, always a ghastly sight with his swollen feet and the classic raspberry lesions of yaws on his face, sat miserably in a pirogue, bound like me. I greeted the boy as cheerfully as I could, but the frog-man struck me across the back of the head. He ordered me to remain silent and get into the bow of the canoe. We pushed off upstream.

Sliding along in the sun, I felt content, except for the cuts on

---

*This section of Casper's diary is undated, and seems to have been put together after the fact in late November.

my wrists from the liana. It was not until lunchtime had come and gone that I realized there was no food in the pirogue. Frog-man kept paddling in the silence.

At dusk, the Mashmish came to an end in a vast marsh. We stumbled out of the canoe and watched him beach it on solid ground. Then he led the way along the mucky margin of the swamp. Khramuphu quickly fell behind and out of sight. Frog-man ran back to him and dragged him by the ear until we were all together again. Khramuphu was groaning from fear and barely able to stand.

Apparently oblivious, Frog-man looked at us sternly and proclaimed: "This is the first day of the world. No villages have yet been built to shelter us, no women to feed us, no mats to keep us dry."

Then he cut loose our hands and permitted us to drink from the marsh. He urinated, and we followed suit. The sun set like a Day-Glow mango. Sleep came quickly despite the damp.

The second day, we continued without food, slogging across the marsh until we came to a lunar field of boulders with green striations and standing as high as six feet. Nothing lived here. Few men had ever seen it. This was the beginning of the Tumuc-Humac Range. Khramuphu moaned as the moonless night began. Two days without food. We slept on flat, cold rock.

The third day, Khramuphu wrapped his feet in leaves and tied them on with some aerial roots he found at the edge of the stone field. Hunger, at first a constant pang, had disappeared. We marched quickly across the plain.

"Now we ascend to heaven," Frog-man announced and sped along a quickly mounting path between huge outcroppings. The vegetation was low and weedy. Water, which we slurped up every few minutes, flowed in a small channel from above.

Quickly, the grade steepened. We lost sight of the high ridge we had taken for the summit and picked footings in what seemed a sheer black wall flashing with mica. Frog-man soon had moved far ahead. I was glad to be following Khramuphu, who had to stop and "change shoes" as the rocks wore away the original leaves. Wisely, he had carried a supply in reserve. The delay also permitted us to rest.

That night we slept on the ridge, shivering from the cold and the wind. There was still no moon.

Foggy dawn held us to a crawl the next day. Lightheaded now from fasting, we inched along the ridge for an hour, knowing in mortal terror that a misstep would send us pitching down a thousand-foot drop we could make out when the fog lifted, as it did for only seconds at a time. It was these sudden and brief periods of visibility that began to stimulate eidetic powers in me. The world was flashing and so did I.

I don't know any other way to put it. Some of the things I saw as I walked along that needle-ridge I really saw. The cotton-wadding fog lifted, rolled away, revealing the drop that first time, and I know it was real, the vile black crater dropping off below and, then, as you looked up, the spike was there, the gnarled shiny obsidian spike standing straight up in the middle of the crater and rising half a mile.

But whether I saw the blood-red flower that snapped in and out of view in a blink of green tendrils and whiskery trailing stamens, that I can't say, because I know that I just couldn't have really seen some of the other things I "saw" up there, the tree that screamed or the plaid dog who recited the prologue in heaven from *Faust*.

Then I fell over Khramuphu, who was resting his feet. Tying on new leaves. I looked at the bloody soles, but they had turned to callus. I showed him, but he shook his face and finished applying the leaves, knotting them tight.

Frog-man strode out of the fog, angry, hissing at us. Instead of going back the way he came, he jumped over the edge.

"Hurry up," he called through the mist from the ledge where he had landed a few feet below. We followed, slipping through the wet, unearthly plants, down the crater wall, choking from blasts of sulphurous air that poured out of hidden fissures, slashing hands and feet against the sharp lava. Down and down and down, yielding up hundreds and hundreds of precious feet of altitude.

The world turned soft and black. We had hit bottom in several feet of fine volcanic dust, sunk to our knees and thrown up an inky sandstorm. Then, climbing to the surface of the crater floor, sooty-faced and drained, we lay on our backs and looked upward where the sky cleared and lit up the monster cavern: black floor, black spike sprouting from the middle, green walls and a circle of blue at the top of the cone.

Frog-man had lost his mask in the descent. I recognized him as T'infa, one of Suri's mother's husbands. He brushed himself off and went to the spike. In a few minutes, he returned with his hands full of pebbles, which he gave us to hold while he traced out a large circle on the ground.

Taking back the pebbles, he walked to the center of the circle, closed his eyes and spat the pebbles from his mouth in various random directions. When all of them had fallen, he set about making a complicated series of lines and marks determined, as far as one could tell, by the arrangement of the pebbles and the length of his shadow. After what must have been an hour, he had located two points and motioned us toward them. At his direction, we lay down on our backs with our heads directly over the points. And then he buried us, to our necks, in the black dust. We watched him walk off silently, until the mist closed over him and left us in a timeless prison without normal days or nights.

Sometimes, the sky above would break into blinding light. Rain drizzled on our faces, with hourly regularity, or so it seemed, and gave us some meager relief from thirst. But for the most part during those days, or hours or weeks, we saw nothing but mist and the insides of our own eyelids, fearing to move— T'infa might be anywhere—fearing to stay still.

Spidery land crabs scampered across our faces in a migratory horde. Flies bit us incessantly. And the volcano rumbled might-

ily below. Khramuphu whispered through the fog—his first
words for who knew how many days: "Mitma, are you still
there?"

"Yes."

Silence again.

The next time the mist lifted, I saw a gold flower grow out of
the black and turn its face toward me. It leered and spoke in
a whistling voice: "Alan, you must absolutely give this up. Escape. Now." Fog swept over it. My legs were stone. I urinated
under the dust, warming my thighs. Sleep followed or at least
I closed my eyes. . . .

. . . A thin woman in tightly fitting flower-patterned slacks
comes and sits beside me. "Thank God, Jack has gone away for
a while to play touch football with Bobby and Sarge. Now you
and I can really talk.

"Don't you think that *we* are the Henry James and Edith
Wharton of today?"

She makes a dramatic gesture with her very long hands and
pirouettes around me, coming to rest again at the point where
she first appeared. Now she is wearing jodhpurs, high black
boots with spurs, a herringbone hacking jacket. Hair tied in a
bun, she shakes her rhinoceros-hide crop testily and, lapsing
into her Sorbonne French, murmurs melancholically: "N'irons
plus au bois, Les lauriers sont coupés."

She leans down and caresses my forehead. Her mouth
brushes my hair, and I notice the pores on her nose are large.
This excites me, for it hints at other flaws and proofs of fleshy
imperfection. I pull her down to me roughly and tug at the
jacket's rough tweed, hard, so that the single button pops. Next,
I tear at the mannish button-down Oxford shirt.

She struggles halfheartedly, pummeling me, digging her Miss
Porter's School ring into my cheek. Between clenched teeth, I
mutter: "La fille de Minos et de Pasiphaë."

"The most perfect line in all of French poetry, if not perhaps
the most beautiful," she purrs, ceasing all resistance. The shirt

is unbuttoned now, and I pull it away to reveal a Berlé delineator on a pale ivory chest tattooed in red, white and blue. The letters spell out "ALL THE WAY WITH JFK." . . .

. . . A 1935 Rolls-Royce Silver Wraith V-12 Saloon bumps across the lava and stops next to me. Cheqchiku in whiteface leans out of the open window, saying: "Once there was no sun and moon, but we didn't care, because we were young and beautiful, and there was plenty of money and booze and we danced on the dunes all night barefoot, would you believe, until the police came and made us stop. I was still blond then. My God, I was beautiful. If it had only lasted, but nothing lasts, nothing good or amusing or sweet. My hair didn't last. The money ran out. The dancing came to an end. And now look at me. Look at me.

"I blame it all on Roosevelt. He stopped the music and turned us all into sparrows, plain little brown things that drink water and cause no commotion. But I was meant to be a bird of paradise with glorious tail feathers. My heart is too big for a sparrow's chest."

She opens the door and floats through the air to a point directly over me and a yard off the ground. "But we have survived it all, haven't we, Mitma? And you go on with your silly composting in spite of the sun and the moon, in spite of everything. Look at you now, covered with manure up to your neck. How can I ever take you with me to the cotillion?"

The smell of manure pours upward. Flies buzz around my head and something bites me underneath the surface of the dung that now buries me. I struggle frantically and manage to get my arms free.

Now for Cheqchiku. As she swoops over me again, I reach up, grab her by the foot and start to pull her down. "Hands off," she cries, "you'll get that stuff on my feathers, and I'll never be able to fly again."

I pull harder and, with a sudden tug, bring her down on top of me with a splat. The impact transforms her into an Isaac

Gellis salami, the kind that Greenspan used to get from his parents in the mail. Carefully, I begin to peel off the protective layer of cellophane. . . .

. . . At first, she seems nothing more than a very tall woman striding toward me across the black plain. But, as she draws closer, I recognize the famous face and notice the high pleated chef's toque as well as the cayman she drags along behind her. It snaps and flails its tail at the end of a gold chain.

"The cayman," she announces shrilly, "is a highly prized delicacy among the peoples of the Amazon. Americans rarely serve it, which has always made me wonder if we're as civilized as we like to think. Cayman is so delicious and easy to prepare; I want you to try some soon. The French who settled in Cayenne always ground it up and made it into mousse, but I'm going to show you the way the natives do up their cayman. It couldn't be simpler.

"The first step is to get a large heavy pot and fill it with enough water so that your cayman has enough room to swim easily. Bring the water to a boil and then reduce to a slow simmer." She stops to light a fire of mahogany logs with flint and steel. When the water boils, she flips the cayman over on his back and rubs his stomach until he falls into a trance. Then she picks him up to put him in the copper caldron. First try, she drops him on the lava, but, undeterred, she goes after him again and, this time, he falls into the water with a big splash that sends scalding water all over the tall woman.

Unfazed, she continues the demonstration: "Now, when you think your cayman is done—forty-five minutes is usually plenty of time—scoop up a paw and press it between your fingers like this. If the flesh gives easily, he has cooked enough. Drain the cayman now and let him cool.

"The next step is to pull his claws out. A wrecking bar is a very effective tool for this. You see. They just slip out. And don't throw them away. The Xixis, who gave me this recipe, never throw anything away. They use cayman claws to make necklaces like the one I'm wearing. Isn't it pretty?

"Now we're almost done. With your machete, lop off the head and then skin the cayman and clean out his insides, making sure not to cut open the gall bladder.

"I like to save the skin for making handbags, but there just isn't much to do with the head besides dumping it in your village river. There we are; ready to go. Just check your ax to make sure it's sharp and then let fly. Cut the cayman into pieces about one-foot square and heat them up in five or six gallons of fresh water, without salt."

She collects the cayman pieces and puts them into the pot. Fifteen minutes pass. I see her reach into the soup, pull out a rib section and start to gnaw on it. Brown juice trickles down over her apron, which seems to annoy her or at least to bother her enough so that she takes off the apron. Underneath it, she is wearing patch Madras Bermudas and a Lacoste shirt. She ladles out a serving of cayman and its cooking liquid into a Royal Worcester tureen and brings it to me.

"Voilà," she quavers, "Ragoût de caïman à la mode de Kuva. Bon appétit."

She bends down with the tureen, but it slips from her hand and falls toward me. Rearing up to fend off the stew, I am temporarily blinded by the hot broth. She tries to comfort me and starts to stuff a morsel of paw into my mouth to distract me from my pain. It tastes like chicken, but it makes me gag and I push her away with my hands.

Suddenly my vision clears and I see that my right hand is pressing against her bosom, directly over the appliqué alligator.

She is braless and, as I press her flesh between my fingers, it gives easily. Her nails are short and will be difficult to remove with the wrecking bar. . . .

. . . "So I told the Master that, Christ, they couldn't expect me to go on paying board *and* the dues at the Fly, now that my father's taken a bath in Chrysler warrants. So he agreed to let me move off campus next term. Of course, I can't afford to rent an apartment in Cambridge either, and the college won't let me live at the club. That's why I came to see you, Casper. You seem to have a perfect setup here. No cost. Plenty of fresh air. The only thing I can't figure is how do you take a shower?"

Khramuphu's complexion has cleared. He is wearing a J. Press suit and a very wide Hasty Pudding tie. He sits on a Triumph motorcycle and sniffs white powder fastidiously off a $100 bill, which he obligingly holds under my nose. I inhale and feel reborn, every pore suddenly rechanneled and flushed out with after-shave lotion.

The feeling goes away quickly. Khramuphu leans forward on his big bike to give me another sniff. It's even better this time, like a superorgasm with the whole body turned into a penis.

"You turkey," Khramuphu says. "Don't snort it all. I want some." He pulls the bill away and sniffs from it. A few seconds pass in silence.

"You see, that's the polite way to do it. You've really got a lot to learn in the way of manners. For instance, you could at least sit up when someone comes to pay a call."

He helps me move some of the lava, and I stand up. A gust of wind blows away the sooty ash that clings to my letter sweater and chinos. I straddle the back of the Triumph. Immediately, Khramuphu roars away through the mist, cornering recklessly, bounding over fissures, and after several hours he suddenly does a wheelie, which dumps me onto a hard, asphalt surface, the tarmac at Edwards Air Force Base.

We walk together into the Officers' Club and sit at a table in a sort of rathskeller. A waiter serves us banana splits with sprinkles though we had ordered beer and Slim Jims, but as I start to object, the lights go out and a woman appears on a small dais in the center of the room, bumping and grinding to the Everly Brothers record of "Bye Bye Love." She is naked except for a spangled G-string, pasties with spinning tassels and an Iroquois mask. When the record ends, she takes off the mask. It is Suri.

She notices Khramuphu in the audience and calls him up on

the stage. They kiss, and while "Toy Bell" by The Bees plays, they start to make love on the floor under a revolving colored-light wheel. I rush up and push them apart, but two M.P.s knock me down.

"You shouldn't have done that, Mitma," Suri says, as the M.P.s frog-march me into another room. It is empty except for a low circular table holding a dozen or so bowls of various colored liquids. Suri comes in and joins me at the table. She wears an Air Force general's uniform now.

"Tell them to let me go," I say to her in Xixi.

She acts as if she doesn't understand what I am saying and tells the M.P.s: "You'll have to pull it out for him. This savage has probably never seen a zipper before."

One of the M.P.s, a redhead with freckles on his hands, opens my fly and stretches my penis out over the table. He then proceeds to dip it in each of the colored liquids, waiting after each dip until the dye dries. He is very systematic, stops to wipe up a few spilled drops with an immaculate khaki handkerchief, and finishes up the decoration of my member with a dash of chocolate sprinkles.

Finally, he lets go, and I stand there drooping, while Suri and the M.P.s laugh. I gaze ashamedly at the floor, only to realize that my feet are covered with water. The room seems to be filling like a pool or an aquarium. Minute by minute, the level rises, but the M.P.s are unable to open the door. I look back at Suri. The water is up to our waists by now. She has started to swim—toward me, toward my penis, which is leaking vermilion and russet and ocher into the rising tide. She raises her head out of the water, revealing the filmy eyes and spiky teeth of a piranha. The teeth snap open and shut, churning up foam. She swims closer. . . .

Guavas. T'infa brought guavas to us in his arms on the morning the sun broke through into the crater. How many mornings had passed between T'infa's departure and his return I couldn't say, nor does it matter. I only know that my dreams in the lava bed came to an end with the smell of fresh guavas and that T'infa had to dig us out of the black sand because we were too weak to move and couldn't even stand once we were free but had to eat on our knees and then sleep out the day and the next night before we could even think about walking again.

And the morning after the guavas, T'infa returned from whatever refuge he sought when he left us, bearing coconuts and a rabbit. He stood before us and proclaimed: "You are born. You have survived the pain of birth. Now you must be purified of the pollution of birth."

He set the food to one side and built a large fire. As it blazed up, he began to chant, really to growl, and kept up the noise until he had seen to it that one long branch lay with only its slender point in the fire and that two earthenware bowls had been filled with a pale green liquid from a gourd.

"Now we will cleanse you from all four sides," he said, lining us up side by side behind him. We marched around the fire, sweating from the combined heat of the sun and the flames. T'infa, always chanting, stopped us on the north, east, south and west of the fire.

Then T'infa pointed to the blaze itself, now leaping to waist height. "Across in one leap," he commanded. I backed up a few feet, ran and cleared the flames easily. Khramuphu, used to failure in physical tasks, ran and balked and wouldn't try again until T'infa kicked him. This time he flew across, but fell back just far enough to singe his left hand. He howled from the pain.

T'infa showed no pity. He advanced with smoking branch in hand and aimed the red point of that carefully prepared poker at Khramuphu's chest. The boy stood motionless and took the stab on the breastbone. It knocked him back on his haunches. T'infa held the point there long enough to send fumes of charring flesh through the air to where I stood drowning in sweat and dread.

Now T'infa moved toward me. It was impossible to run. The fire was behind me. I was too weak to outrun T'infa. The point touched me with a rip of pain. I smelled the hair on my chest flare away and the skin burn down to the bone. T'infa at last threw away the poker, but the pain continued.

Half-conscious, we followed T'infa to the prepared bowls. He sat us down in front of them, and we drank the fetid potion to the bottom. Within minutes, what must have been a powerful emetic in the liquid forced us to vomit wildly.

When we finished and lay spent on the sand, T'infa spread ashes over the vomit. He stopped chanting and smiled, I thought, with relief. "You are clean now and can eat with the other frogs."

Now he prepared the rabbit, skinning it, dressing it, spitting it on a green stick. While it roasted, we debauched on coconut milk and meat and threw the husks high in the air. The rabbit was gone in minutes.

All this took only a few days, but the exaltation lasted on for many more. We left the crater the day after the ceremony, but we stayed in the forest near the headwaters of the Mashmish for almost three weeks, allowing the burns to heal and our mood to wind down. We made a congenial trio, hunting and trapping together in forest and river, for Khramuphu's yaws had remitted, T'infa had dropped his awful solemnity—to joke with him now seemed the highest of privileges—and I joined them without reservation in their jungle idyl. Indeed, it was never a question of joining *their* idyl. The time belonged to all three of us, by right, as certified adult frogs in the Xixi nation.

No foreign cerebrations interfered with my enjoyment or cut me off from my brothers, until the moment we rounded the last turn before Kuva.

"Now, Mitma," said T'infa from the stern of the pirogue, "now that you are cleansed and purified by fire and sweat and vomiting, cleansed in mind, purified in body, you can understand why we have no need for the special rites of other tribes who fear garbage and aka."

VII

DEAD LETTERS

[Since no mail got through to Kuva in November or December of 1963, these three letters did not catch up with Alan until it was too late for them to matter to him. R.S.]

November 25

Dear Alan,

By now you must have heard about the assassination. Or have you? Somehow I can't believe that even Kuva is so isolated that the news hasn't got through yet.

Just in case it hasn't.

President Kennedy was assassinated in Dallas three days ago. He was riding in a motorcade and a sniper shot him. Today, he was buried in Arlington Cemetery.

The whole country is on the point of collapse from emotional exhaustion. All normal life stopped a few seconds after the bullet hit him.

Already there are a dozen theories of who did it and why. A nut acting alone. John Birchers. Cubans. And so on.

To me, the fascinating and frightening part is the national reaction, the collective paroxysm, the way all of us have sobbed in unison, twitched as one body. Is it authentic emotion or are we manufacturing the grief in response to the lugubrious pie-ties we've all been absorbing off television for the past 72 hours?

It's more than just nil nisi bonum. The country has been told to mourn, by all three networks, and it is mourning, like mad, but this is a televised wake, and we are all acting as if we were on camera. We're monitoring our own reactions, watching ourselves on the tube being interviewed by Dan Rather.

Jackie, as usual, set the standard of performance. She even had a special costume, a blood-spattered dress that she wouldn't take off for hours after the event, not until "they" had seen her in it, on the Cronkite news.

Don't misunderstand. I feel horrible, as upset as I've ever been. But I ask myself how the feelings can be real. I never loved Jack Kennedy. Before this, he always struck me as a light-weight, a smooth, attractive nouveau riche with unlimited ambition.

I hissed Teddy at commencement in June. That was really hissing Jack, who boosted his dumb brother into the Senate. I hated JFK for the Bay of Pigs and, more so, for the missile crisis. It was my life he was risking to prove his macho.

OK, so I'm a Radcliffe bluestocking who's found out she's a sucker for soap operas in which the dead hero is a Harvard man. But what about all those millions out there who hated the man for his wealth or his religion as well as his politics? What about all those people who didn't vote for him and know they didn't get their Nixon because of a sleazy deal for 100,000 votes in Chicago?

They're crying too. Everyone is.

"Where were you?" is now a code question. It means, "What were you doing when you heard he was shot?"

I was in an operating room at the Mass. General watching the great Philip Mungerberg perform an appendectomy. He's a professor of surgery at Harvard Med. I wangled an independent study program this fall. I get one course credit for, listen to this, writing a paper evaluating antiseptic standards in three Boston hospitals. A man at the Public Health School who graded Chem. 20 last summer had some grant money for the project and couldn't find anyone else to do it. Anyway, what I'm really doing is escaping the Square for a few hours each week and trying to see if I actually do like medicine.

Mungerberg is one of those flashy surgeons who ought to wear a black cape lined in red satin. Mephistopheles with a scalpel, a matador twirling toward his bull while a thousand eyes widen in admiration. Well, a couple hundred eyes at least, medical students in the amphitheater waiting to see the inventor of the Mungerberg procedure do his stuff.

I was standing on the floor of the OR in white gown and mask, notebook at the ready, pretending to be recording my observations about surgical antisepsis, when I noticed that the students in the amphitheater had all started to get up. I could hear them talking to each other through the glass wall. Then, a black scrub nurse came running into the OR crying, and told us. Mungerberg, who had just finished his McBurney's incision, set down his scalpel and stood still for a moment looking at the rest of us. Then he turned back to the patient, slipping his hand into the small opening in the abdomen, and finished the operation in record time. He strode out of the room and we all dispersed to the nearest television.

I've barely moved since I got home and planted myself in front of the set.

My father called for the first time in months. He wanted to be sure I was all right and to tell me he was expecting an appointment in the Johnson administration. Good old Dad. The only man in America with a dry eye and his mind on himself. Or at least the only man honest enough not to fake grief even to his daughter.

That got me back on the road to normalcy. Tomorrow, classes start again, which should help too. But I am mostly marking time until I take off for darkest Qatab. Expect me in Gé on December 20. No one seems to know what time I should be arriving or if there's any place to stay. Please try to be there to meet me.

Love,

Missy

November 25

Dearest Alan,

This is the first time I have been glad that you are overseas. You are so fortunate to be far away from all this sadness and violence. I am thankful for that and also proud that the assassination didn't happen in Flint. This is such a law-abiding city. One of the few.

What is happening to our country?

If the president can't travel safely, who can?

But I don't want to depress you. You must have cried yourself to sleep all weekend like the rest of us. What do the people in your village think? I suppose they're used to killing. Still, even headhunters can thumb their noses at America now.

Mrs. Kennedy was noble. I wish she had changed her dress sooner. But, other than that, she is the model widow. So refined and beautiful. To lose such a fine, loyal husband—I can hardly bear it.

We thought of you often over the last few days, your father and I. We miss you terribly. Please write more often. Even a post card would do. The picture alone would be worth it. We know so little about what you are doing. Are you getting to know the people? That is an opportunity not to be missed.

How are the other volunteers?

Have you met any interesting girls?

I have so many questions, don't I? Daddy and I can't wait to see you again, and so, here is our big surprise, we are going to meet you in the spring in the Virgin Islands. More about that later.

In the meantime, stay healthy.

Love & Kisses,

Mommy

P.S. I have sent you more vitamin pills by surface mail. By the time they get to you, the others will be almost used up by my calculation.

UNITED STATES EMBASSY
Chiotteville
Qatab

November 26

Dear Casper,

This is an entirely unofficial communication. Please burn it in the tribal campfire. I would not like to see it turn up in the *New York Times* by some unhappy accident, and neither would you.

No doubt you have heard by now that President Kennedy was assassinated by a sharpshooter in Dallas on the 22d. This has disrupted our work here entirely, as you might imagine. Chiotteville has been in official mourning ever since. Tukuna sent a wreath of flamingo feathers. One spends one's time either accepting commiseration from the locals or trying to explain to Roucou politicians and their wives that this does not confirm as reality the impression of American life they have gleaned from western movies at the Ciné Plaza.

Le Bagne has added Texas chili to its menu.

I tell you all this merely as background. And to prepare you for the mood of the capital on your return.

You have been reassigned, on my authority, to a teaching job in Chiotteville. I have not been able to clear this through Peace Corps, Washington, thanks to the utter chaos there, but you can count on their approval.

Here is why.

1. With Lyndon Johnson in the White House, it is no longer useful or necessary to keep you out of harm's way in Kuva. Obviously, you would not have the bad taste to tell your little story now. And it would cause no real harm anyway.

2. Far more important is the fact that Tukuna has signed up with a German uranium-mining outfit. The contract is an exclusive prospecting arrangement that keeps everyone else out for the next 10 years. As a result, we no longer need your report. In fact, we don't even want the Krauts to find out that you exist. Let them make their own contacts with the Xixi.

Privately, I don't want to be responsible for exposing your gonads to any more milliroentgens of radiation than they have already absorbed in a lost cause.

You will have to make your own travel arrangements. Presumably, you can hire paddlers as far as Gé. We will pay for the plane from there back to the Paris of the South Caribbean.

Fold your tent posthaste. Good luck.

LIVINGSTON KAUFMAN

VIII

ARS AMATORIA

November 26. T'infa dropped us, almost literally dropped us, without a fond word, on the shore of the piranha quadrant. No one greeted us, and we walked quietly to the bachelors' barracks, a dank place no larger than the usual house but more dilapidated and almost completely unfurnished. It doesn't even have mats. It's the Xixi version of the kind of rental cottage you might find in a cheap American resort area. But after the crater, any roof will do.

Food arrives mysteriously twice a day. And the empty bowls disappear just as mysteriously. I have been sitting outside the barracks for two days now writing down my memories of the initiation, but I have yet to see a piranha "waitress" deal with our room-service repasts.

Khramuphu has been gone most of the time sowing his wild oats among the tapir ladies. The poor guy doesn't know when to stop; he's wearing himself to a frazzle, and falls in an exhausted heap when he gets back here. I've barely been able to talk to him since we got out of the pirogue. But he hasn't stopped smiling yet, even in his sleep.

I would have hopped over the fence myself much earlier if I hadn't had to bring this journal up to date. But now it's time for Mitma to show his stuff. Really, though, I feel quite monogamous and can't wait to see Suri. I hope she's not angry that I've waited so long, but I didn't dare let those memories slip away before I put them on paper.

Off I go.

November 27.   I don't know what I expected would happen when I crossed the fence, but it did not turn out to be simple finding a woman to work my bachelor's will with. The tapir village was pursuing its normal life. Dinner had just finished in most houses. Fires were guttering. There were certainly no women waiting for me with open arms. They were all indoors.

I walked through the village, feeling quite silly and certain that those giggles I heard were aimed at me. Eventually, I braced myself and entered Suri's house. Her mother told me she had gone to another village the day before to visit friends. I thanked the woman, who seemed to want me to stay—was she coming on to me?—and went outside again.

An old man was sitting on a flat rock in the middle of the village. He called to me, so I went and stood by him.

"They think you are afraid, because you stayed so long on the other side. Are you afraid?"

"No. But I don't see any women outdoors. I don't want to just go bursting into a strange house."

He laughed softly. "Mitma, that is just what you will have to do. Did no one tell you that the custom is for a bachelor to creep silently into the house of the woman he wants? If he can touch the inside of her pillpa without waking her mother, then she is his for the night."

Fine. But which house to pick. I knew practically no one among the tapirs except Suri. She was gone. Playing it cool, I was sure.

But I couldn't just slink back to the barracks now. It had been months. . . . Missy *would* be here in a few weeks. . . . I picked a hut at random, probably because it had a new roof . . . a middle-class American to the end . . . walked over to the door in the darkness . . . careful not to crack twigs underfoot . . . and, I confess it without (much) shame, I crawled in like a cat burglar. There was just enough light to make out the outlines of three adult bodies. Two of them were partly interlocked. The third was farther into the room. I edged forward slowly . . . long braids . . . She lies face down, snoring lightly.

My hand was poised like a cobra head, but I struck more slowly, checking aim twice and finally gliding down to my target. Hot, warm, moist. It was definitely a pillpa, but my intended continued to snore. I penetrated further. She was cavernous, and still dead asleep.

Exasperated, I rolled her over, pushed the knees apart and prepared to begin.

"Welcome, Mitma," she said, wide awake and grinning at the success of her put-on. "I am Lachiwana."

She was a Maillol fantasy of rolls and pudge. I fell on her with the crazy lust of four months' abstinence. She wrapped around me. I was completely engulfed, folded in and wrapped up, a morsel of meat stuck in a blob of fat, slippery, warm, rich fat.

I could see absolutely nothing now. I only felt and caught breaths when I could. But I could hear Lachiwana's parents talking to each other. They spoke too softly for me to understand them, since my ears were well buried. But the tone was, at least, not loud and indignant.

Quick release. I slid away to solid ground.

"Thank you," came a voice from near the door. "You have been kind to my daughter. Will you please her further and lie with me?"

I looked toward Lachiwana. Her face was still hidden in shadow, but I distinctly heard her say: "Don't worry. She is good, better than an erqewacha like me."

This proved to be true. The old woman was pendulous but imaginative. My enjoyment, in the early moments of our bout, was diminished by premonitions of a vengeful assault from the father, but he actually fell asleep after a bit.

November 28.   I slept even later than Khramuphu yesterday morning. He seems to be tapering (tapiring?) off. At any rate, having managed to stagger out of the barracks, I resolved to make a reconnaissance tour of the tapir village by daylight in order to gather useful data for my next nocturnal foray, and to see at last what my companions of the previous night looked like. Tonight, I would at least have a mental picture of my partner(s).

The tapirs were all busy at their daily tasks and, therefore, on display for me. I particularly admired one girl who was rolling cassava balls in front of her house, whose location I carefully noted. Then I paid a social call on Suri's mother, who had no information about her daughter and hurried off on an errand.

With no further obligations for the afternoon, I ambled casually by Lachiwana's house and had my worst fears confirmed. She was a Rubens in shape, but her face was a tragedy: nose askew, eyes beady, cheeks bloated. And the mother was an out-and-out crone, 50 if she was a day and looking more like 80.

They invited me in for a drink. Although I wanted to run away, I couldn't refuse a beer from the family I had fucked the night before, could I?

So we had our drink. But I drew the line there. Dinner? No thank you, Lachiwana. My clan needs me for a special monkey hunt tonight. What about tomorrow? I'll have to see.

I fled across the fence and spent the rest of the day paddling a pirogue up and down the Mashmish, downriver of Kuva. I didn't want to see anyone.

At nightfall, I hurried back to the tapir quadrant and strode, fully upright, into the house of the beauty I had earlier seen rolling cassava balls. With no modesty whatever, I reached under her cache-sexe, touched the magic spot and began immediately to claim my rights. She hit me in the face. Her father and brother then threw me headfirst out the door.

"This is the wrong house, akatanqa. Lachiwana lives over there."

"But I prefer your daughter," I whispered, hoping not to be overheard and provoke a scandal.

"Then why are you promised to Lachiwana?"

"Promised?"

"You lay with her mother, didn't you?"

"Yes. She asked me to."

"Of course she did. And then you accepted a drink of beer from the family the next day, didn't you?"

"Yes."

"Well, then, you're engaged. So stay away from Wakan."

And that was that, a short and lugubrious bachelorhood. No chance to try for Suri or even Wakan. It was 300 pounds of Lachiwana for me. Definitely akatanqa.

November 29.   I had no one to turn to except Khramuphu. He listened to my story with great glee, declared me a llachiq and then asked my why I was sulking in the barracks when I should be over with the tapirs.

"But I don't want to see Lachiwana," I said, exasperated with him for misunderstanding my feelings.

"Obviously," he retorted with disdain. "You want to break off the engagement, but you can't do that sitting here."

"How can I break it off? I didn't know I could do that without causing trouble. How do I do it?"

"I'll take care of that. Just come with me."

We walked into tapir territory until we came to a tumble-down hut by the water. An old man sat at the door plaiting feathers for a mask and crooning to himself.

"Good morning, Layqa," Khramuphu said to him. "I need your help."

Layqa looked up slowly and waited.

"Mitma, my initiation comrade, has been bewitched by a fox who has forced him to behave strangely since we came to the piranha barracks. The fox came into his body and lay with Lachiwana and her mother two nights ago. Can you frighten away the fox so that Mitma will be restored to himself?"

Layqa seemed to agree to exorcise my vulpine demon. He chewed some coca leaves hurriedly, donned a horrific mask and led me to the center of the square settlement. At his bidding, I sat down, facing east, toward the forest. He began dancing around me.

This was the signal for a crowd to gather. I noticed also that Khramuphu was circulating among them, spreading the word about my fox-incubus. There was much shaking of heads and pointing to Lachiwana's house. But when a woman from the crowd carried the news into the house, no one emerged.

Meanwhile, Layqa had begun shaking me by the shoulders and kicking me as he danced, harder and harder. The crowd shouted to frighten the fox. Layqa eventually went into a partial trance, convulsing and hooting. And after he had gone on like that for quite a while, with the crowd growing more and more excited, he ran at me and thrust a berry, a red berry, into my mouth. I swallowed it half-chewed, because of the bitter taste, and soon after, I blacked out.

The sedative or whatever it was must have been quite powerful; I did not come to until dusk. The crowd quickly reassembled to watch me get up and weave away uncertainly to the barracks. "Mitma has returned from the dead," someone said. "Layqa has scared away the eqeqo."

December 1. Ever since I got rid of my fox, I've been much too busy to write. The bachelor's life in earnest is a full-time job. How did Casanova squeeze in the time to write his memoirs?

To date I have run through every tapir woman who is unmarried and past puberty. That makes five, not counting Suri, who is still away from home.

Some general observations: The old adage about all women being the same in the dark has been definitively disproved.

Each one of my experiences was subtly, and sometimes not so subtly, different from the others. Wakan, for instance, is a screamer and biter; was she showing off for her three fathers, who sat watching us in the moonlight? The others were less dramatic, but I think of them individually, remembering this one's way of rolling her hips or that one's low grunt at orgasm. They all seem to have orgasm. And they appear to have been taught that it is proper for them to be on top. Wakan refused to be rolled over into the missionary's position. "I'm no paytu," she said.

At any rate, this is a miserable way to choose a wife. Even if you come by in the daytime to talk with one of them, their mothers dominate the conversation and spend the whole time trying to seduce you, batting eyes and letting their hands fall on you as if by accident. In context, it makes sense. As I have learned with stunning clarity, it is sleeping with your prospective mother-in-law that counts, not making love with your future bride. So the old ladies are extremely frisky and forward.

Now, of course, I understand why Suri's mother was nice to me at first and then avoided me. I wish Suri would get back. This merry-go-round is killing me.

December 2.   I paid a call on Suri's mother and told her I was starting to worry about the girl. She had been gone so long.

"You really want to see her, yes?"

"Yes, I miss her. She is my best friend in all Kuva."

"I think I know how to speed her return. Will you come into the house? There is something I want to explain privately."

I followed her in. Her two husbands were napping in back. Suri's mother turned toward me and untied her cache-sexe.

"Now, you must decide," she said, "if you want to have Suri or not. She will not come back to Kuva until you have made up your mind."

The husbands were awake now, watching. If I walk out now, I thought quickly, I may as well leave Kuva altogether. I will be stuck in the bachelors' quarters until I "marry" someone. My work can't go on as long as I am unwelcome in the frog quadrant, where my manioc crop is growing. The bachelor life is impossible to keep up for long anyway. I like Suri much more than the others. She obviously feels the same way, which is the reason for this ultimatum. The Xixis have no concept of romantic love; khuyay exactly describes my feelings for Suri; so I can enter this match without dishonesty in Xixi terms. Khuyay is enough for them. And why should I worry about some Western standard of emotional exaltation that I have always said I didn't care about anyway? The only moral snag in all this is that I don't expect to stay here for more than my Peace Corps hitch. But even if I don't take Suri with me when I leave, she'll only be sixteen and perfectly capable of marrying again. For that matter, she can remarry while I'm here. Besides which, I've told her I will be going back to America and that she would be miserable there. I'm taking my chances in this deal; she can take hers.

And so I lay down on the mat. And Suri's little mother smiled. Her two husbands smiled. I smiled too as she moistened herself with spit and crouched down over me. It was over quickly for both of us. I kissed my mother-in-law while she helped me dress. And then we joined my fathers-in-law in front of the house for the ceremonial drink of beer to seal the contract.

Everyone else in the tapir village gathered to help us celebrate. Everyone, that is, except Lachiwana, her family, and, of course, Suri. One of her fathers, the real one I think, went to fetch her.

Tonight is my last night, then, in the bachelor barracks. Khramuphu thinks I have behaved stupidly again, since I sacrificed my freedom before even "lying" with my bride. I have told him about my earlier friendship with Suri, but he still thinks I should have insisted on sleeping with her at least once before "pouring honey on her mother," as the idiom goes. Maybe he's right. Oh well, it's my cultural background coming out. I've even caught myself wondering whether Suri is a virgin.

December 3. Suri and her father returned today at lunchtime. I had been waiting at her house for them all morning, even honeyed her mother once more just for good measure, in the missionary position, which made her blush. If we keep this up, I may be the father of my own brother-in-law. You can't be a success at coitus interruptus 100 percent of the time. But I suppose I'll have to stop doing it to the old woman anyway now.

Suri arrived finally, shy but triumphant. We exchanged the same meaningless remarks that lovers exchange everywhere in public. And then we went inside, all five of us. But when I told Suri in English that I wanted to be alone with her, she looked hurt. "Are you ashamed of me?" she asked.

And so, while Qhaphra, Suri's mother, prepared lunch and her fathers enjoyed their corn beer apéritif in the corner, Suri and I consummated our marriage. We lay down and kissed until I was ready, and then, because she *was* a virgin, she borrowed some fat from Qhaphra to help things along, rubbing it on both of us and apologizing for her inexperience in a combination of Xixi and English. "It will be over soon. I am wamera; so you will have to t'ikannay me. I hope it does not annoy you."

"It will not annoy me," I said, as she came to rest on me, pushing down. Nothing happened, so I tried to help her, but she would not allow me to touch her with my hands. Qhaphra came over to assist, and between the two of them they forced the barrier to break, to tear apart suddenly so that Suri and I were one flesh.

"Añañau!" she shouted as I pierced into her. She looked like a victorious warrior. And the blood ran from her freely for a few seconds, after which it seemed to be reabsorbed into her as she declared her womanhood in joyful undulation.

By this time, Qhaphra had gone back to pounding manioc for lunch. But a little while later, when Suri and I had finished, she drew me aside and asked: "It was good sallallay? Yes? It will get better. She learns quickly. You know that already, I think. So we will plan the sawa ceremony for tomorrow."

December 4. Suri, who alone among her people understood that I was truly not a Xixi or even an Indian and that I had not the slightest familiarity with cultural facts that even a child ought to know, spent the morning briefing me on the details of the imminent rite, so that I would not pollute the two clans with some unintended gaffe. She seemed to enjoy reversing our earlier roles, teaching me instead of being taught. I also recited the traditional English marriage vow for her.

By American standards, we were a couple with unusually few doubts about what the future would bring. We would live in Qhaphra's house, assist with the routine tasks of the village and perform the traditional duties owed to our clans. Also, we would continue our efforts to clean up Kuva and the Kuvans. In short, we had none of the fears and quandaries that are the normal lot of newlyweds in the postliterate world. And we certainly did not have to worry over money.

The afternoon passed quickly, although we were required to stay in the house while elaborate feats of geomancy, cooking and decoration took place in the center of the village. We did not, however, fill the entire time of our ritual isolation with carnal reaffirmations of our coming union. Some of the afternoon was spent that way, yes. But we are a serious pair and did not neglect the obligation to paint each other with whorls and polygons that stood for the four clans, the heavenly bodies and the river.

Original designs were also permitted. Taking my cue from Suri, who gaily inscribed my buttocks with matching American flags (my people's totem sign, I had once explained to her), I drew a heart on her stomach with our first names written inside. It seemed best to leave out the conventional arrow to avoid misunderstandings.

Drums began at dusk. Qhaphra came with a huge blanket of flamingo feathers and covered us with it, from head to waist. And then, as one ungainly beast with pink plumage, we moved blindly out of Qhaphra's hut toward the sound of the drums. Suri poked me playfully in the crotch, making me double over. I grabbed her hand and held it until we had crossed a trench dug in the dirt and the feather blanket was raised over our heads and carried off by many people to its normal resting place in one of the huts.

A great fire rose and waved its flames before us. Children danced in the shadows. I looked toward the river, where a procession of torchlit canoes was crossing from the frog village. Warramunga and Cheqchiku landed first and walked slowly to the fire, leading several goats and bearing the jaguar skins from our hunt. The other frogs gathered behind them to watch them hand the goats and pelts—Suri's bride's price—to Qhaphra. There was a short and purely symbolic argument—the price had been prearranged—that was resolved when another goat was led up from the rear of the frog delegation. Applause followed and everyone sat down except Suri and me. Warramunga, as chief, then recited the traditional marriage myth:

"In the early days, as you may have heard, men and women did not know one another and lived separately. Like the birds and the snakes, they feared each other and made great efforts to hunt separately. The women, in fact, finally gave up the dry land altogether and dwelt in rivers as fish.

"Two brothers, at that time, were alone in the forest and feeling lust. They were, in fact, the only men left on earth, because the others had died childless when the women sank into the rivers. The brothers knew this and were lonely as well as hungry for sex.

"As far as they knew, the women had simply escaped to another part of the forest; so they had hunted them far and wide without success. Indeed, they had looked so long that despair had begun to darken their minds.

"And so, when they came to the bank of a slow, wide river, they were glad to find two otters, whom they thought, in their innocence, were women.

" 'Come here,' they called to the otters, 'and we will make love to you.'

" 'And how will you do that?' asked one of the otters.

" 'Don't be coy,' one brother answered. 'We will put our penises into your ears, as men always used to do to women.'

"At this, both otters laughed. 'We are not women, you silly boys. Women live in the river and have no ears, only fins. If you want to make love to them, you will have to catch them first.'

"The brothers then clambered into the water and trapped two women in a net. They pulled them on the shore and prepared to ravish them. One of the otters was standing nearby and, seeing that the men did not know precisely how to proceed, said: 'If you want to make love in the old way, you should use their vaginas, but be careful.'

"The brothers looked closely at the women and discovered that they had sharp teeth in their pillpas. Thanking the otters, they pulled out all the teeth and went ahead with their lovemaking at last. The women conceived and gave birth to children, two girls, who walked on the earth with men and did not grow teeth between their legs.

"And that," said Warramunga, "was the beginning of our way of life, which you, Suri and Mitma, pledge to continue tonight and from now on."

This was the signal for the dancing to begin. Suri and I stood in the middle of the crowd, waiting until they had all lost themselves in the rhythm. Then we ran through them toward the river, chased by all the tapirs and frogs, who shouted at us as we jumped into a pirogue and paddled away downstream.

Soon the noise died away. We embraced and drifted until the sound of rapids warned us that our voyage was done. I tied us up to an overhanging branch and returned to Suri who sat waiting for me, for her husband.

She looked at me earnestly and said: "Till death do us part."

IX

OUT OF

THE WOODS

December 7. I have been living with Suri in Qhaphra's house for two days now in a kind of euphoria, savoring each detail of our new existence. We swim and eat and putter at chores. Suri practices her English with me regularly and has already reached the point where she can discuss almost any subject quite intelligently. She seems to have spent every minute of my initiation reading my books.

This comes as a great relief—her being able to converse in English—because I have spoken so much Xixi that I am beginning to forget English vocabulary. More than that, I have needed someone to express thoughts to, my "civilized" thoughts that can't be articulated in Xixi. I find that if I go for more than a day or two without writing in this diary or talking to Suri seriously in English, I get ferocious headaches. They were the hardest part of the initiation—after the ritual was over and we basked and fished together, I would keep trying to force some idea into Xixi in order to share it with T'infa or Khramuphu. The frustration must, physically, roil the brain in much the same way that repressed rage eats away at the stomach.

Which brings me to my abdominal symptoms, Doctor. My tummy is very tender these days, especially when I move suddenly. It's probably nothing, just a pulled muscle, possibly from nocturnal gymnastics.

Enough hypochondria.

I had meant to use this time to describe what Suri and I did today. She asked me why I hadn't gone for my things yet, my trunk and my books and the rest of my paraphernalia. They were all still in Cheqchiku's house. Suri said that she wanted to finish looking through the *Oxford Book of English Verse;* she had bogged down in it without me around to help her with hard passages.

In the back of my mind, I had known I should go back to the frog quadrant, if for no other reason than courtesy to Warramunga and Cheqchiku. But I had put off the trip because I didn't want to see what had happened to my fields and my compost heap while I was away in the Tumuc-Humac and the bachelor barracks. The newlywed life was too pleasant to sully with hygiene.

This morning, when Suri pressed me to go, I felt there was no way to avoid the trip. And so we paddled across the river and began the day with a visit to my parents. They gave us a warm welcome. Warramunga kissed me, saying how glad he was that my bachelorhood had lifted and that now we could talk and touch and, he hoped, go hunting again.

Cheqchiku insisted on touching my initiation scar. She ran her palm over the circle of white, hairless skin where the hot poker had sizzled. "I'm the first in my family to have one," I thought. Some people brag about being the first in their families to finish college or wear shoes. I have a ritual cicatrice. Mother will be so proud.

Warramunga walked with us back to the fields. On the way, we passed the site of the compost, which had obviously not been replenished with fresh waste material for several days. No one said anything about it, but Suri was looking guilty.

I forgot the composting failure as soon as we came to the experimental field. Everything had grown magnificently, higher and thicker than the surrounding crops.

"It worked, Suri," I said excitedly.

"I knew it would," she replied, stroking my arm.

We both looked at Warramunga. "It's an excellent crop, Mitma. You and Suri did a fine job. But growing is only half the job. Now you must harvest."

I exploded inside. What did he mean? It hadn't been just an excellent crop. It had been incredible and it had proved my point about composting and everything else. Suri told me later that the amount of dysentery had risen sharply in the frog village during November.

I was furious, but I didn't say anything then. It was the wrong time. Instead, we pitched in with the harvesting, all afternoon, until my right arm hurt almost as much as my stomach. I could barely move my trunk of books, when we started back to the tapir quadrant at dusk.

Suri said: "I'm sure that Warramunga knows that you're right. He just doesn't want to disrupt his village over something he thinks is not very important."

"Chiefs are supposed to lead their people toward better lives," I snapped.

December 11.   More stomach pains this morning, and the right arm is still sore too.

Suri asked me why I had come to Kuva. I once explained to her how many days it would take to get to Boston by pirogue; so she understands that I didn't just wander over from another part of the forest.

I said: "I wanted to travel and see people different from my own, to learn from them and help them if I could."

"But you will go home someday, won't you?"

"Yes."

"And what will I do?"

"Come with me if you want to."

"But I know nothing. I'm a black savage. I just read about my people in that Peace Corps book you have."

"Don't pay attention to that. The man who wrote it is an idiot.

You are much more sophisticated and intelligent than he is."

"But I would still not know what to do in your country."

"What wouldn't you know? How to use a telephone or flush a toilet? All that is easy to learn."

"I mean other things. Things from books that you know."

"You could go to school. I'm sure Radcliffe would take you as a special student."

"What is Radcliffe?"

"A very good school for bright girls like you."

"What does it look like? Are there many skyscrapers?"

"The buildings are not large but very solid, with stone roofs. They stand near a wide river. Wise old men tell what they know to the young, and there are thousands and thousands of books to read."

"Do savages ever go there?"

"Many."

I did not mention shoes and snow and bras or checking accounts. If I could hunt jaguars, she could get used to all that. And imagine how wonderful she would look in clothes.

This conversation took place on the way to see Warramunga. I was determined to make him see the light. He was simply too clever and humane not to understand the importance of proper waste management and sanitation. Suri wasn't so sure.

We found him working on his hunting darts. "Hello, son," he said, smiling. "I am going for jaguar soon. Will you come with me to bring me luck?"

"Yes. I'll be happy to."

"The harvest is almost finished. We'll plant the new crop, and then we can leave."

"I hope you are going to compost." (I had coined the word "compostuy" weeks before.)

"Mitma, you are too old for this nonsense. When you were still a child, I humored you. Now you have grown up; you have your scar; you're a Xixi, one of us. Why should I baby you?"

"But, Warramunga," said Suri, "you saw the crop."

"Everyone is lucky sometime. Rain and sun make good crops. And we have doctors like Layqa to cure disease. Only fools hoard their aka."

"Warramunga, I come from a country where one man can feed fifty others with his crops, because he uses fertilizers that are like compost. Almost no one ever gets dysentery."

"But I am a Xixi. And so are you. You went through the initiation, you speak our language better than anyone else in the village. I don't know what village you came from or why your skin is so pale, but you are certainly a Xixi. How else could you have learned so quickly to live as we do in Kuva?

"The answer is that you always knew and only pretended to know other things. Someday you will tell me why. But for now I am happy with you in spite of this game you insist on playing.

"Also"—he scrutinized one of the darts as he spoke—"I would not want compostuy even if I had learned about it from a real foreigner who had great powers over his own fields. In our fields, we know the correct and safe way to coax manioc from the ground. New methods from afar are dangerous. Compostuy, for instance, asks too much from the soil, and if we should keep on with it, the soil would rebel and take revenge."

December 12.   Severe abdominal pains today. Also headaches and tenderness of right arm. Extreme nausea makes writing any more impossible.

December 13.   Chayapu . . . chills . . . must have hampi . . . manan mikhuy . . . write English . . . I am American and can recite the pledge to the flag, name all state capitals. . . . Pisipa . . . fever raging all day. . . . Suri says eye was in complete state of muspha all day, very phuchu . . . qañañaña. . . . Fever must have been extremely high. It's remitted now . . . enough for me to write anyway. My symptoms don't fit anything that I know about. . . .

. . . Layqa has bled me, made me vomit. Suri sits next to me, sure I'm going to die. Probably I will and that doesn't matter to me but it will to her—and to the village . . . uranium . . . sooner or later, they'll get impatient and come in for it anyway . . . too much money to resist . . . destroy Xixis to make safe for miners . . . forty-niners . . . and who ever really met a girl named Clementine? . . . Paddleford, *This Week* . . . this week my last . . . warn Warramunga, double double U's.

My head is clear now again. Warramunga came in to see me. I've told him about the uranium. He didn't believe it so I re-couched the explanation and turned it into a prophecy: "Men with skins like mine and outlandish costumes will come by air looking for heavy stones underground. Don't fight or join them. Move away. The jungle is very big. They only want the stones. If you fight, they will burn and kill with powerful weapons that shoot from far away. Don't make friends with them for they will steal your nuna and change everything until Xixis are not Xixis."

He smiled patiently, sadly, and left. They have given me up for dead, except for Suri. She reads to me when I come out of the fever, from *Religio Medici*, figuring it has medicinal powers, I guess. Her pronunciation is excellent, but I can't believe she understands a word of it.

The miners are bound to come. I looked at my radiation strip the other day. It was registering radioactivity, definitely. Not enough to hurt anyone, but enough to make this much more than just any stretch of remote river bank.

It's not hard to predict what will happen. Warramunga will never believe me. He'll fight them. I know it. But the blowguns will only hold back Tukuna's dollar-greed so long. And if it's not dollars, it will be francs or sterling or yen. What's the difference? The jungle will die under their feet and the Xixis will disappear as Xixis. Survivors, the strong ones, may end up shining shoes in Chiotteville if they're lucky. . . . . . . ñausay ña . . . manan . . . must stay awake . . . horrible dream takes over when I sleep . . . on White House lawn . . . President Kennedy rolling Easter egg, which breaks and hatches into black worms. Band plays "Hail to the Chief." I salute, hand over heart. Secret Serviceman then grabs me by the scruff of the neck and starts pulling me away. JFK stops him, personally. The crowd moves back. He pins the Medal of Honor on my chest, right on the scar. No pain. He reads Congressional citation: "To Mitma, for his great contributions toward the friendship of America and his people, the Xixis of Qatab." . . .

December 18.   How long have I been lying here? The room stinks of my vomit. I can't sit up from weakness. Suri mops my forehead with cold water. Layqa, I dimly remember, has been running through his medicine chest, to no avail. I've got to figure out what's wrong with me. . . .

Suri found my Peace Corps medical guide stuck to the back of the *Iliad.* I've got amebic liver abscess. All the symptoms click. I'm an adult male with a previous history of amebiasis, and now: pain over the liver, referred pain in the right shoulder, intermittent fever, chills, nausea, vomiting, weakness and no jaundice. The brain, it says, is sometimes infected through the bloodstream. Fatal, unless treated with chloroquine, emetine or metronidazole.

At first, I thought of sending Suri to Gé to get some flown in. But, even if they could understand her, they'd never pay any attention. We've got to go together. I can't ask Warramunga to give me paddlers. He'd think I was delirious. Xixis don't go to Gé when they're sick.

Suri seems to understand what's going on. I've written a message for the missionary in Gé, in French, in case my brain has collapsed by the time we arrive. She calculates it will take her three days to get there.

Qhaphra is telling her now not to go. I will die anyway, she says, and there are too many rapids. Suri tells her there is strong medicine in Gé, that she has to get me there. She is a strong girl,

a good paddler. She can drag the pirogue around the rapids
with a liana rope.

Qhaphra's husbands grudgingly agree to carry me to the water. Suri brings food for the journey. We push off, and I begin
to feel sick again. I vomit into the Mashmish, the river I was
going to clean up. . . .

. . . Told Suri once again about emetine, so she can ask for it
if I go out of my head completely. Picked emetine over the
other two because it's easier to say O say can you spare a dime
that tries men's nunakuna—first fruits of their wilderness, star
of their night who hold dominion over palm and pine—arwiq
. . . arwiq, a bottle for kitchen and bathroom . . . emetine, Suri,
give me emetine or give me sipi, I don't care if we never get
back at the ranch, in a month, in a year uranium will be only
as good as your weakest link on: you can llachiy some of the
runaka some of the time but the añas, who was very apussonqo,
knew better and changed himself into a man with a thumb that
could grasp sticks. Then he pulled down a dead branch from a
nearby elm and used it to thrash his mother and his father and
all his aunts, before he left the world of foxes forever and set out
to make his fortune. He walked as far as he could on his hind
legs, but eventually he grew weary and lay down to sleep in a
tulip glade. The next morning trumpets blared and a pack of
hounds, crook-kneed and dewlapped like Thessalian bulls, pursued añas's scent, for he still smelled like a fox. He heard them
give cry and scrambled to his feet. They drew closer; he ran and
ran, through copses and thickets, tearing off his fur on brambles,
tumbling into a briar patch and emerging with only the hair on
his head, under his arms where the thorns could not reach, and
over his ichu, which he had guarded with one paw. And for this
reason, men wear the waralli today.

Finally, he came to the edge of the forest. The dogs had been
slow in pursuit and must have lost his trail. He could no longer
hear them. He licked his wounds carefully and walked out of
the woods into the sun, which dried the blood and warmed him.

Soon he fell asleep by a rosebush, safe at last and ready to begin his new life as a man. But the hounds found him and devoured his body, all but the bones and entrails, for they were hungry from the long chase and enraged at the sight of a fox who had pretended to be a man. When the hunters caught up with the pack, they saw human bones and guts strewn over the ground. In fury, they attacked the hounds and threw their bodies across the Potomac. The following spring, cherry trees sprouted on the same ground.

December 20

Dear Sue,

Primitive is really primitive!

I'm in a little river village called Gé, the most unbelievably awful place, waiting for Alan to arrive. Imagine what his village must be like, if he thought I should meet him here, where there is no electricity, the houses have dirt floors and everyone except for the missionary, a French Lutheran, goes around naked and filthy. The little children would make you cry. Their bellies bulge from malnutrition; flies nest on their faces. The heat is overwhelming. How has Alan stood it? Who can he have talked to all this time?

Frankly, I'm quite worried about him. He's never late even for trivial appointments, and he knows what I've had to go through to get here: fly to Trinidad, wait three hours, fly to Chiotteville and spend the night there—that was horrible—you just would not believe how dismal that city is—and then I flew in here in a plane that must have been bought in an army surplus auction. It bumped through every cloud for miles and then the illiterate pilot, who could see I was terrified and seemed to enjoy it, descended to treetop level and stayed there for the last hour.

Finally, we skidded into the water, and I've been sitting on the river bank waiting ever since. That makes five hours, except for tea with the missionary, le Révérend Brise, who speaks no

English, of course, but makes up for it with gestures like touching your hand when he passes sugar. Actually, I don't blame him for being horny. Who wouldn't be out here, all alone?

I suppose he does it with the native women, saggy tits and lice and all. Poor guy. The men are much better value, small but muscular. I suppose I could get used to it after a while. It would be the real test of whether sex has to be accompanied by some kind of social relationship.

The river is gorgeous. (No pun intended.) I'm writing this from the brink of a high cliff that overlooks a postcard waterfall. Naturally, there are no postcards here, but, come to think of it, if they built a little hotel, this might turn into a fabulous spot for tourists. You could set up some sort of organized excursion in canoes, with guides.

I guess that's what Alan has in mind for us to do. I don't see how we could stay in this town. I hope he has two air mattresses.

Anyway, he isn't here yet and it's getting dark. Brise invited me to stay with him, which I guess I'm going to have to do. He does have screens, real beds (he mentioned that at tea) and kerosene lanterns. Also, he's got a shortwave rig. And if Alan isn't here by morning, I'm going to radio for a hydroplane charter so that I can go look for him. Something must have gone wrong.

Love,
Missy

December 21.   It is my duty as a wife to continue my husband's diary. He is too sick to write. Later, he will want to know what happened to us on the river. I am sure he will be well soon. Please, Mitma, do not laugh at the way I write.

It is hard for me to remember all the words for things. I am very tired.

This afternoon we were still on the river. I was almost too tired to paddle, but the current swept us along. You had not been awake or spoken for two days, except once. I was carrying you around a rapids through the forest. You said my name and told me it was too late.

I keep on paddling, because you must get the emetine from the missionary at Gé. Then there is a great noise. At first, I think: it is a big rapids. I am afraid. But the noise comes from above and then in front of us. A giant bird, I guess at first. I know nothing. Of course, it was an airplane. I have read about them in your books. I did not believe in them before this one.

Maybe I am sick too, I thought. But then a woman got out, a beautiful woman wearing clothes. She spoke English. She called you Ellen. Then she cried and said to me: "I will take him to a doctor."

I said: "We are almost in Gé. I will get him there easily in the canoe. The airplane will make him sicker."

She said: "No. The plane will take him to a real doctor far away."

I said: "They have emetine in Gé. That is enough."

She said: "What is a matine? It must be some native remedy. You are a good girl, but he needs to be in a hospital. Help me put him in the plane."

The man with her came to the canoe and took you away. I said to the woman: "My clan will kill you if you steal Mitma. He is my husband."

The man pulled you out of the pirogue. I tried to stop him, but he was too strong. The woman said: "Are you really his wife?"

I told her yes. We were just married. You got sick in the stomach and then the head. I said you needed emetine. She did not understand me. I ran after her to the plane.

I said: "Take me with you. I should not leave a sick husband with strangers."

She said: "When he is well, if he wants to, he will come back. There is no room for you in the plane. I'm sorry."

I have cried, cried, cried. You will not fly back to me. I don't think. I did not give that woman your message. It was for the missionary. Now they will not give you emetine. You will be dying. I will be a widow no man will want. I let my husband die. I will never see you again, and we will never go to America.

December 29

Dear Sue,

I did finally have to radio for the hydroplane. We flew upstream along the Mashmish and located Alan in a dugout canoe paddled by a native girl. He was stretched out, comatose, obviously very sick, muttering unintelligibly in what I later found out was the local language. The girl, who spoke a childlike kind of English, was doing her best to get him to the mission downriver.

I was half-dead myself from traveling and the heat and culture shock. There I was in the most terrifying place you can imagine. Alan looked simply awful—matted hair down to his shoulders, dirty, with an ugly scar on his chest. We had to get him out of there immediately. The girl struggled with the pilot. She didn't want to abandon Alan, because, she said, she was his wife.

She couldn't have been much more than 12. Slight, sweet-looking, but fierce all the same. We left her there shouting something I didn't understand then. Now I know she was telling us to give him emetine. But I'm getting ahead of the story.

By the time we took off I was hysterical with fear and, to be honest, jealousy. We could have made room in the plane for the girl, but I hated her so much for claiming my man. If only I had kept my head and done the civilized thing, brought her along, she would have eventually gotten her message across. Instead, we flew off to Chiotteville, swamping her canoe with the waves from our propeller's backdraft.

I slept all the way back. Fortunately, the pilot had radioed ahead for an ambulance. Alan was still in a coma when they took him away on a stretcher to the hospital. A man from the embassy named Kaufman drove me there in an official Cadillac. He assured me that the hospital was modern, the surgeon had been trained in Lyon. Alan would be all right.

We waited for an hour. Then Dr. Subric came out to talk to us. He had a trim little mustache, a glistening manicure, gold-rimmed, hexagonal glasses and a crewcut. Very self-assured. About 30. I hated him instantly.

He lit a cigar. Kaufman lit a cigar. For a minute I expected someone to pass brandy and cordials. Alan was dying. Subric put away his monogrammed cigar clipper, commiserated with Kaufman about the bad effect of the dampness on Havanas, and then launched into the most pompous little diagnostic lecture I ever want to hear.

"Messieurs, Dames," he began, staring like a hungry crocodile at my knees through the smoke, "this has been a most difficult problem. I have personally performed as exhaustive an examination as is possible under the circumstances. Before all else, it has been necessary to treat the patient's fatigue, and, therefore, I have instituted intravenous feeding. Ideally, we would wait until the young man regained consciousness in order to take a case history, but I am afraid that his physical condition does not permit us the luxury of further delay. Decisive action is imperative.

"Accordingly, I have had his blood analyzed in the laboratory of this splendidly equipped hospital. I have put him through a battery of X-rays and other tests, but it was the simple expedient of physical examination that uncovered the answer to the diagnostic riddle. You, Mademoiselle Rand, had alerted me to the possibility of pathology in the digestive system. The testimony of a native informant, I believe.

"I palpated the abdominal area. When I probed what is technically known as the right lower quadrant, the patient groaned quite audibly. He also exhibited the psoas sign, which is to say that even comatose as he is, he indicates pain when his thigh is hyperextended. Add to that, if you will, the lab report of leukocytosis and mild fever, and you must conclude that he has acute appendicitis. Voilà!

"As to the loss of consciousness, we can only speculate with respect to causation. He undoubtedly has some other tropical disorder, which we can treat medically after the appendix has been removed. I operate immediately. The prognosis is excellent. The appendix has not yet even ruptured. I recommend that you both get a good night's sleep and return in the morning."

Kaufman left for a party at the French Embassy. Some sort of pre-Christmas celebration. I told him I would stay in the hospital, nap in the lobby. I would never get to sleep in a hotel. Kaufman shrugged and went off. Subric excused himself.

I tried sitting in the lobby. It was deserted at that hour, midnight. Nothing to read except a month-old copy of *France-Dimanche* with headlines about Farah Diba. I tried to imagine what Alan had gone through in the past few months. Would I even know him when he came to? Would he want to go back to his "wife"? I would just have to hang on and hope he recovered completely, recovered his old identity as well as his health. All I could do was wait.

No, that wasn't all. I could at least make sure Subric knew what he was doing. After all, I had observed appendectomies performed by the great Mungerberg. Why not watch this one?

No one saw me go into the fire staircase and walk up to the surgical floor. They only kept one operating room running at night. Subric had said he would use the big one where he demonstrated for student nurses during the day. I stole into the empty amphitheater. The lights were off so that no one in the OR below could see me through the glass partition. I took a front seat and flipped on the amplifier for the sound system.

Subric and a black scrub nurse were getting their equipment ready. Alan lay flat on his back on the table, naked, pubic hair shaved, already anesthetized. Limp but very tan.

Subric picked up a scalpel with the same bullfighter's flourish as Mungerberg. You could see he had picked the right specialty. He loved to cut.

In went the blade, one little slice, the McBurney incision, just big enough to let him get at the appendix. He reached for it with one rubber-gloved hand. The fingers disappeared inside Alan. Something was wrong. Why wasn't he cutting the appendix? The hand came out. Subric looked at his fingers. I thought I heard him say, under his breath, "Merde. Un choix."

But what kind of choice? What was going on?

Subric went over to a sink by the wall, washed his gloves and threw them out. He put on a new pair and returned to Alan's side. He looked slightly pale under his tan as he sewed Alan up. Sewed him up. No appendectomy, no exploratory incision to see what *was* wrong if he hadn't found appendicitis. Subric was giving up.

He finished the sutures and strode out of the OR. I ran down the fire staircase and intercepted him in the corridor. "Why did you stop in the middle of the operation?" I shouted at him as walked quickly away from me.

He looked back angrily over his shoulder. "What are you talking about, Mademoiselle Rand? Why don't you get some sleep?"

"You know exactly what I'm talking about. I watched the whole thing from the amphitheater. You just opened him up and then sewed him together again."

Subric stopped, scowled. "Come into my office." He looked suddenly tired.

The office was stifling. They had turned off the air conditioning hours ago in that part of the building. He motioned for me to sit down. "You shouldn't spy on people, Chèrie."

"That wasn't my original plan. I just wanted to observe. I'm a premed student. I spend a lot of time at home at operations, especially appendectomies, but never the kind you do."

"In your climate they don't probably find too many liver abscesses."

"What?"

"Amebic liver abscess. It's an extreme and often fatal complication of amebiasis. Without a good case history it may be very hard to distinguish from appendicitis. If you do an appendectomy by mistake, you run a high risk of bursting the abscess. Infection then washes all over the peritoneal cavity. Death is almost inevitable."

"And you burst Alan's abscess, didn't you, poking around trying to figure out what was wrong with him after you'd felt his appendix and knew it was normal?"

"Unhappily, yes. I knew what I'd done when I pulled my hand out and there was anchovy paste on my fingers."

"Anchovy paste?"

"The classic abscess exudate, the stuff that comes out of the abscess. It resembles essence d'anchois in color and texture. First time I've ever seen it."

"Oh, that's what you were saying. I thought you said 'un choix.' What do you propose to do now that you've, shall we say, revised your diagnosis?"

"I'm sorry to have to say this, but there is almost no hope for him. I've put him on antibiotics and, of course, emetine—"

"Oh, my God. That's what she was trying to tell me."

"Who? What are you talking about?"

"The girl. On the river, where I picked him up. She told me to give him emetine. I didn't recognize the word. I assumed it was something in her language."

Subric looked relieved. He realized that I was too guilty in my own mind now to think about suing him for malpractice. We had both killed Alan. I wanted to vomit.

Instead, I went to the hotel and slept, until dinnertime the next day. Then I went back to the hospital, to Alan's room. He was still in a coma with the IV bottle hanging over him. From time to time, he would speak in that odd, clicking language, but his vital signs got weaker by the hour. It was only a matter of time.

He lasted a week. I sat by him day after day, useless. Kaufman came by after lunch regularly. And there was a woman Peace Corps Volunteer who had been friendly with Alan in training. They must have been lovers. She always brought flowers, big gaudy anthuriums, and tried to draw me out about Harvard and New England. One afternoon, she insisted on reading some very weepy poetry to Alan, who, of course, heard none of it. I left the room.

Sitting with her was uncomfortable even without the recitation. Rivals in grief. And all the time I kept thinking that Alan's real widow was off in the jungle somewhere with no way to get to him. Kaufman wouldn't hear of bringing her to Chiotteville. I asked him about it once. It would be impossible to find her, he said. I knew he didn't want to increase the scandal by flying in the dying Volunteer's aboriginal child bride. I didn't think I could face her either. So no one went for her.

Instead, we tried to find a man called Ituru, who knew Xixi, the language Alan was speaking. Kaufman discovered that he was guiding a government expedition in the interior, but he couldn't find out when they were supposed to get back. On what turned out to be Alan's last day, Kaufman brought him into the hospital. He wrote out an English paraphrase of Alan's last words. Here they are:

Do you think you can wait a little while longer? I am very anxious for Suri to hear you play the Scriabin. She is bashful still about coming here to the golden room. . . . Thank you, yes, the dictionary is well on its way. I'll be happy to show you what I've done when Suri and I get back from London. . . . The one in the Frick is magnificent, but I still prefer "Cupid, Love, Folly and Time." . . . No, I'm sure there's no connection. The point of the myth is not culture versus nature but culture versus culture. That's why it's a recently invented myth. Modern history has intervened and upset their sense of isolation. Both the flamingos and the ants represent culture, two definitions of it. And they kill each other off. . . . Where can Suri be? . . . But they both make things. The flamingo harvests tobacco; the ant builds houses. They both have their own culture, but they have no common language, and so they misunderstand each other. . . . Maybe I should call her. Something may have happened. . . . Suri? . . . Where have you been? We've all been waiting. . . . Let's talk later. He's sitting down to play. . . . I'm sure the jaguar hide will go beautifully over the mantel, dear, and I'll certainly write your mother, but I can't do it tonight. I'm too tired. . . . The Scriabin *was* beautiful. But my stomach bothered me so much I couldn't enjoy it. It must have been that quiche at Chez Jean. I'm sure I'll be better in the morning. . . . Good night.

And then he stopped talking, forever. It will be a long silence.
Love,
Missy

Epilogue

Nothing is ever really over and done with. Alan died, but he left loose ends trailing behind him on two continents. And none of us minor characters in his life lived happily ever after. My troubles have been basically financial, and I want to thank you, dear reader, for helping me out with your $7.95. That reminds me. If you haven't been able to do the crossword puzzle on page 79, you can arrange to receive the answers by sending $1 (check or money order) and a stamped, self-addressed envelope to the author, c/o Harper & Row, 10 East 53rd Street, New York, N.Y. 10022.

As far as the rest of them are concerned, I can't tell you much. Sarah Ashton is working in Las Vegas as a "hostess." She writes me long letters full of poetry and spicy stories. I salute her for surviving.

Missy Rand is a practicing surgeon in Connecticut and active in liberal causes. I wouldn't want to say that Alan's botched operation inclined her toward a specialty seldom entered by women, but one can't help speculating. She has never married.

The only time I've seen her since 1963 was at Alan's funeral. She flew back with the body to Flint and stayed for several days with the Caspers after the ceremony, a model daughter-in-law in spirit if not in fact.

Looking back on those two days I was in Michigan, I remember only two things clearly. The first was a direct impression. Missy was radiant as only a child widow can be. She had acquired an independent role, as Alan's chief mourner, and there would be no floundering for her in the marriage market. She was bereaved and could do as she liked.

The other important memory seems important only in retrospect. We, Missy and I, were alone for a few minutes in the cemetery, after the interment, when everyone else had left. She had knelt by the grave, and I waited for her to get up so that I could walk her back to the main gate, where the cortege was waiting. As we made our way through the monuments, I asked her to tell me about finding Alan, where and how she had done it, what he had looked like and said—all those rude questions that not even Alan's parents had ever asked her.

Her answer was short and betrayed no emotion. She had waited in Gé until she was sure something was wrong. Then she had chartered a plane and discovered Alan paddling alone, semidelirious, a few miles to the south.

And so when I set out to collect material for a life of Alan Casper, I had no idea that he had been married or that Suri existed. Quite frankly, I started out with the idea of doing an article for the *Alumni Bulletin* and using that to justify a tax-deductible trip to the Caribbean via Qatab. Even that idea didn't occur to me until nine years after Alan's death, when I happened to read in a guidebook that you could hire canoes for organized river safaris in Qatab. The trip was billed as the cheapest jungle experience in the world for New Yorkers, because Chiotteville was so close to La Guardia and the paddlers would work for almost nothing.

Before I left, I phoned Missy to get the name of Alan's village. She didn't seem to want to tell me, but I wormed it out of her. After that, I was suspicious.

By the time I got to Qatab, it had changed utterly from the hellhole Alan experienced in 1963. Uranium had brought wealth to Chiotteville in the form of international luxury hotels, a flamingo-pink presidential palace designed by Edward Durell Stone, and a television station. The interior of the country had been thoroughly crisscrossed by aerial mapping teams from the uranium cartel, Uranus G.m.b.H. But the myth of Qatab's wildness was perpetuated by the national tourist office, which had discovered that the country's reputation for completely unspoiled primitivism was its trump in attracting visitors from older, played-out cultures.

One of their posters displayed a blond man in a bush jacket surrounded by nude black women with bones through their noses. Another showed a white woman with her foot on a dead jaguar.

My tour group was composed entirely of American big-game hunters and two of their wives. They had all been shooting in Africa and Alaska before and would have preferred to return there, but a business recession had cut into their travel budgets. They shot at anything that moved, parrots, caymans, flamingos. That we all got out unwounded was a minor miracle.

I had had no problem in finding a tour that passed by Kuva. They all did, because it had grown into a major center on the Mashmish since Uranus set up headquarters there in 1965. The mines were more than a hundred miles inland, but Kuva was the closest point to them on the river.

As we arrived, our guide sketched in the recent history of the village. The first party of geologists had been slaughtered to the man, and their bodies were dumped during the night on the airfield at Gé. Then Tukuna, to save his face with the international financial community (the guide spoke of defending Qatabian honor), had sent his army to burn Kuva to the ground. Uranus moved in as soon as the ashes had cooled.

The prospectors threw up a boomtown of Quonset huts, which are still there. And later Uranus built a rough-and-ready inn for travelers, where my group spent the night. I was glad to be able to take a shower after several days of sweltering in a dugout canoe.

Out the bathroom window, I could see an occasional black child passing in the street below. And in the distance, a few shacks where the last of Kuva's Xixis lived in apparent squalor against a jungle backdrop. A bulldozer rumbled somewhere nearby.

The shower ran lukewarm no matter how you adjusted the tap. But it still refreshed me enough so that I felt like a walk before dinner. Two of the hunters from my group had the same idea, and we ended up strolling uneventfully around town. But on the way back to the inn, a black woman came out of one of the Quonset huts with a thin little boy.

They were a remarkable pair. She wore a cotton dress, blue gingham with puffed sleeves, and shoes. The boy looked almost white, and his hair had so fine a texture and fell so straight that no one could mistake him for anything but a mulatto.

At that point, I had no direct suspicions about who they were. Westernized Qatabian women and mulattoes had been common enough in Chiotteville. But they did strike me as a possible source of information about Casper. So I went up to the woman and started to question her in French. She spoke with great fluency, too fast for me to follow her. When, however, she realized from my accent that I was American, she switched into a pure but stilted and noticeably literary English.

It was Suri, of course. The boy, called Alain, had been born eight and a half months after Casper's death, and there could be no doubt, especially if you noticed his razor-edged physiognomy and arrowy torso, that this was Alan's son.

Suri and I talked for at least an hour; words rushed from her, overspilling memories unshared for nine years. Most of what she said is in Alan's diary. Indeed, after she had given me those notebooks, wormy and rotting from long exposure to the jungle damp, I realized that she must have read them through many times since the day Alan was spirited away from her. She remembered her time with him exactly as he had written it. Turns of phrase and whole sentences from his diary came out in her speech.

I stayed with her for several days. She lived with the French Lutheran minister, who had sheltered her when she paddled into Gé, hysterical with rage and grief, too tired and ashamed to start back home and wild for some scrap of news about Alan. The missionary eventually converted her (at least to his own satisfaction, and he was easily satisfied where young black women were concerned) and married her. For Suri, the conversion was not an event of great spiritual upheaval, but merely a clear and simple step further into the culture of her first husband. The marriage, for a woman raised to think polyandry the normal pattern of wedded life, meant no betrayal of Alan.

As it happened, Suri was alone for the two weeks I spent in Kuva. The good Reverend had gone on a trip to the mines in search of new souls, and I never saw him.

Suri spent her days trying to conform to her book-learned ideas of what a model American or French housewife should be. She also taught Alain English and French, with textbooks ordered from the Lycée in Chiotteville, so that he could prepare himself to go away to school.

"When we moved back to Kuva," she told me one afternoon over tea and an excellent brioche, "the company had already chased almost all my people away. Warramunga, the old fool, had tried to fight them with blowguns. For him, discretion and valor did not mix, and so, ignoring Alan's advice—why did he never listen?—he brought destruction, rapine and death on his tribe. He was a good chief, but he was born too late.

"In those first months after we settled here in the place where I was born, I grieved for the lost world of the Xixis of Kuva. I helped my second husband as an interpreter. A few of my people, as you have seen, lingered in their all but vanished village. And there were many other Xixis in other villages along the route to the uranium lode.

"Uranus eventually hired me to travel with the advance party that explored the area. I was supposed to 'pacify' them. Instead, I gave them Alan's warning and told them that if they did not move to another part of the forest, they would share the fate of Kuva or, worse, they would see their way of life destroyed by bulldozers and a culture they could not understand. Some listened; some did not. Still, I saved many, who are now resettled deeper in the jungle and, I hope, far from the uranium.

"For me, it is different. Ever since my second husband received the news of Alan's death by radio, I have lived in three worlds, or perhaps a better way of putting it would be to say that my thoughts come now in Xixi, now in English, now in French.

"For Alain it will be different. He is his father's child. He reads the books that came in the trunk. He will study. And some day he will go to Harvard. Then I will lose him, but if I tried to keep him here, I would be killing the part of Alan that is in him. I prefer to kill my part.

"Alan once said he wanted to take me to America, to Radcliffe. That was a pretty dream, but not one of his better ideas. He was, underneath his constant protestations to the contrary, a great romantic. He indulged in fantasies of the impossible. I do not indulge in such fantasies. Except for one. I loved him. I still love him. And I want his son to continue his father's life where the surgeon cut it off. Now you will say to me that there is no way for the boy to slough off his Xixi nature, and that is true. Alain will never turn into a pure American; he will always straddle the gap between here and there. But then he will not really be doing anything that his father didn't do. The difference is that he will be coming at the same problem from the opposite direction. It will be hard, holding the truth of myths and the truth of machines in his head at the same time. But he hasn't any choice. Perhaps it is a great opportunity."

She touched the boy's arm. "I've been teaching you English,

haven't I, Alain?" she said. "Recite the poem you're learning, the one from your father's book."

The boy stood up, not at all shyly, and began to chant:

> Should you ask me, whence these stories?
> Whence these legends and traditions,
> With the odors of the forest,
> With the dew and damp of meadows,
> With the curling smoke of wigwams,
> With the rushing of great rivers,
> With their frequent repetitions,
> And their wild reverberations,
> As a thunder in the mountains?
> I should answer, I should tell you,
> "From the forests and the prairies,
> From the great lakes of the Northland,
> From the land of the Ojibways,
> From the land of the Dacotahs,
> From the mountains, moors, and fen-lands
> Where the heron, the Shuh-shuh-gah,
> Feeds among the reeds and rushes.
> I repeat them as I heard them
> From the lips of Nawadaha,
> The musician, the sweet singer."
> Ye who love a nation's legends,
> Love the ballads of a people,
> That like voices from afar off
> Call to us to pause and listen,
> Speak in tones so plain and childlike,
> Scarcely can the ear distinguish
> Whether they are sung or spoken;—
> Listen to this Indian Legend,
> To this Song of Hiawatha!
> Ye whose hearts are fresh and simple,
> Who have faith in God and Nature,
> Who believe that in all ages
> Every human heart is human,
> That in even savage bosoms
> There are longings, yearnings, strivings
> For the good they comprehend not,
> That the feeble hands and helpless,

Grouping blindly in the darkness,
Touch God's right hand in that darkness
And are lifted up and strengthened;—
Listen to this simple story,
To this Song of Hiawatha!

Appendix: A Xixi Word List*

Achacha	Toy
Achiku	Naked
Achiqyay	Flash, twinkle
Aka	Dung
Akana	Corral, pen
Akatanqa	Fool, dummy
Akawara	Honeycomb
Akay	Defecate
Allachiy	Harvest, scratch
Amachay	Defend
Amak'u	Tick
Amiq	Dull, cloying
Amlla	Tasteless
Anaku	Blanket, cape
Anaq	Tough
Anassu	Concubine, mistress
Anka	Agile
Ankalli	Rebellious
Ankallikuy	Rebel

---

*Assembled from notes made by Alan Casper from August to December, 1963.

Anpullu	Great-granddaughter
Anqosay	Drink a toast
Anyachiy	Warn, urge
Añaka	Candy
Añas	Small fox
Añayniy	Ornament, trinket
Apachiy	Send
Apaykuy	Lead to
Api	Prison
Apussonqo	Proud
Aqllariy	Choose
Aqnay	Work
Aqo	Sand
Aqtuy	Throw, vomit
Aqwa	Needle
Arawa	Pitchfork, gallows
Araway	Hang
Armay	Bathe, wash
Arwi	Rapids
Arwiy	Entangle
Aslla	Scarce
Asna	Malodorous
Asnaq	Pestilential
Asnu	Burro
Assi	Laugh, smile
Assikuna	Joke *(n.)*
Assikuy	Laugh *(v.)*, joke
Assiq	Funny
Assut'i	Whip *(n.)*
Assutiy	Whip *(v.)*
Astakuy	Change abode
Astaray	Move animals from one place to another
Astawan	Much more
Atau	Happiness, good luck
Atauchi	Distinguished, notable

Ati	Bad luck
Atipa	Victory
Atipakuy	Persist
Atiqlla	Requirement
Atiqllay	Require, intimate
Atiruna	Cruel
Atissanka	Prisoner
Atissankawasi	Prison
Atiy	Be able, surpass
Atoq	Vixen
Auka	Enemy
Aukana	War
Aukanakaq	Warrior
Auki	Divinity
Aukilla	Great-grandmother
Awana	Loom
Awanini	Net
Awaq	Weaver
Away	Weave
Aya	Corpse
Ayapaka	Gravedigger
Ayaqra	Cadaverous
Ayawaka	Tomb
Ayawantu	Coffin
Ayawasi	Cemetery
Aycha	Meat
Ayllu	Kinship
Aylluchay	Become related by marriage
Ayma	Procession
Aymura	Crop
Aymuray	Harvest *(v.)*
Aynay	Flower, flourish
Ayni	Return (a favor)
Ayñiy	Contradict, oppose
Aypha	Vague

Ayqe	Escape *(n.)*
Ayqeq	Fugitive
Ayqey	Escape *(v.)*
Ayranpu	Tapir
Aysana	Handle *(n.)*
Aysay	Pull
Ayu	Adultery
Ayuq	Adulterer
Chacha	Toy
Chachi	Severity
Chaka	Piranha
Chakana	Hobble *(n.)*
Chakisenqa	Shin
Chakitaqlla	Plow
Chaku	Hunt *(n.)*
Challi	Sly, funny
Challwa	Fish *(n.)*
Challwachiy	Fish *(v.)*
Challwaq	Angler
Chanaku	Youngest son
Chani	Value
Chaninchaq	Evaluate
Chanqay	Throw, shoot
Chapa	Spy
Chapuqeyoq	Lunatic
Chaqma	Fallow land
Chaqoy	Chop down trees
Chaqra	Arable land
Chaqru	Mixed up, awry
Chaqruy	Mix
Charcha	Screaming
Chayamuy	Arrive someplace else
Chayapu	Chronic disease
Chayay	Arrive

Chaycha	Perhaps
Chaylla	This only, nothing else
Chaynin	This way
Ch'acha	Hungry
Ch'achu	Swindler
Ch'aka	Hoarse
Ch'aki	Dry
Ch'akichina	Towel
Ch'akichiy	Dry *(v.)*
Ch'aqla	Punch, blow
Ch'aqllaña	Clear, transparent
Ch'aqma	Uproar
Ch'amay	Work hard
Ch'aphcha	Talkative
Ch'aphsa	Kindling *(n.)*
Ch'apu	Bearded man
Ch'arwi	Confused
Ch'aspa	Robbery
Ch'aspay	Rob
Ch'eqo	Chisel
Ch'eqollo	Nightingale
Ch'eqtay	Shatter
Ch'illikutu	Grasshopper
Ch'illini	Wink, blink *(n.)*
Ch'illinipakuy	Wink or blink frequently
Ch'illpi	Fragment
Ch'in	Silence!
Ch'ini	Smallest
Ch'ipu	Wrinkle
Ch'ullo	Common cold
Ch'uñu	Dried potato
Ch'uspa	Bag for coca leaves
Cheqa	Truth
Cheqachakuy	Justify oneself
Cheqaq	True

Cheqaqchaq	Truthteller
Cheqchikachay	Coquetry
Cheqchiku	Flirt
Cheqni	Aversion
Cheqniy	Hate
Chichu	Pregnant
Chika	Riverbank
Chikama	Good-bye
Chikuy	Pen in a litter of goats
Chipana	Ring (for the finger)
Chiran	Winter
Chiriy	Be cold
Chischay	Siesta
Choqche	Thin
Churay	Keep safe
Churichaq	Adoptive father
Churichaqe	Adoptive son
Eqeqo	Demon, imp
Eqo	Son conceived by a lactating mother
Erqe	Little boy
Erqewacha	Sexual neophyte, female
Hak'u	Flour
Hallpa	Mastication of coca
Hallpi	Scratch *(n.)*
Hamp'atu	Frog
Hampi	Medicine
Hampiq	Physician
Hamurpay	Guess, suspect
Hanaq	Above
Hanilariy	Yawn *(v.)*
Hanku	Raw meat
Hanpina	Disease that should be medically treated
Hanuk'achiy	Wean

Hapt'a	Handful
Hatucha	Grandmother
Hawariy	Tell stories
Hayaqen	Gall bladder
Hayt'a	Kick
Hichana	Dumping ground
Hik'i	Hiccup
Hisp'a	Urine
Hisp'achiy	Urinate
Hok'o	Damp
Hucha	Sin, misdeed
Huchachakuy	Relapse
Huk'ucha	Rat
Hunp'i	Sweat *(n.)*
Huñinqa	Favorite
Hut'u	Corn borer, dental cavity
Ichu	Penis
Ihma	Widow
Illaq	Shining
Imra	Circle
Iñi	Faith, belief
Ipa	Maternal aunt
Ipala	Great-aunt
Ipiñi	Only child
Ismu	Rotten
Itha	Bird louse
Kachiy	Go out
Kaka	Maternal uncle
Kallpa	Force, energy
Kama	While
Kanikuy	Bark, bite
Kanka	Roasted
Karu	Far

Kausarinpay	Resuscitate
Kausay	Life
Kiki	Similar
Kiru	Tooth
Kisma	Man's mother-in-law
Kiwachi	Woman's mother-in-law
Kullaq	Ticklish
Kullcha	Manure
Kuncha	Man's nephew
Kunti	West
Kuraq	Firstborn
Kuru	Worm
Kusi	Pleasure
Kusichay	Congratulate
Kusipata	Place of happiness
Kutipakuq	Cheeky, pert
Kututu	Virile
K'alla	Small parrot
K'amiy	Insult *(v.)*
K'anay	Suffer high fever
K'anchay	Light *(n.)*
K'askiy	Boastfulness
K'iri	Ulcer, lesion, wound
K'irikuy	Wound *(v.)*
K'umillu	Hunchbacked
K'usillu	Clown
K'utukuy	Lampoon
K'uychi	Rainbow
Khachuy	Bite *(v.)*
Khastuy	Chew
Khatatatachiy	Quake, rumble
Khatatay	Earthquake
Khiki	Mange
Khullchiy	Dig
Khuyay	Friendship, tenderness

Lachiwa	Honey
Lachiwana	Honeycomb
Lakakuy	Fall on one's face
Laqmu	Toothless
Layqa	Sorcerer
Lonla	Stupid woman
Lonqo	Obesity
Loqlo	Fool, simpleton
Luluchuy	Caress with passion
Luluy	Caress
Lunchu	Brother-in-law
Llachapa	Ragged
Llachiq	Dupe (n.)
Llachiy	Dupe (v.)
Llaki	Sadness, pain
Llakimana	Satisfied
Llalliy	Conquer
Llank'ay	Work (v.)
Llanta	Firewood
Llant'achiy	Send to gather firewood
Llant'ay	Gather firewood
Llanthu	Darkness
Llapa	All
Llaphllawa	Placenta
Llaqtamasi	Fellow villager
Llaqway	Lick (v.)
Llausa	Spit, mucus
Llokhe	Left-handed
Lloqlo	Rotten egg
Lluch'i	Bruise
Llulla	Lie (n.)
Llullay	Deceive
Lluthu	Ear

Macha	Beer
Machachiy	Intoxicate
Machaq	Sot
Mach'in	Biceps
Machuyaya	Great-grandfather
Maki	Hand
Makuku	Prudent
Mallaqllay	Fast *(v.)*
Malliy	Taste *(v.)*
Manan	No
Mancha	Cowardice
Manchachi	Ghost, vision
Manchaq	Frightening
Mapa	Beeswax
Mapakuy	Menstruate
Maqchikuna	Laundry area
Maqma	Wide
Maqt'a	Young bachelor
Markachikuy	To let someone take you in his arms
Markaq	First or chief husband
Markasqa	Child of the chief husband
Masi	Neighbor
Masu	Vampire
Mayu	River
Melkho	Adam's apple
Melkhoy	Swallow
Mikhuna	Meal, repast
Mikhuy	Eat
Milla	Nausea
Millay	Nauseating
Mitk'akuy	Stumble
Mitma	Stranger, foreigner
Mitmay	Colonize
Miyuy	Poison *(v.)*

Moqo	Knee
Mosoq	New
Mosqoy	Dream *(n.)*
Much'a	Kiss *(n.)*
Much'achiy	Cause to kiss
Much'apayay	Kiss many times
Much'ay	Kiss *(v.)*
Much'u	Nape of the neck
Muhu	Seed
Mulla	Nephew or niece
Muru	Smallpox, scarlet fever, measles, yaws, dysentery
Muspha	Delirium
Musphay	Rave
Mut'uy	Mutilate
Muyuy	Spin
Nak'ay	Behead
Nanay	Suffering
Napay	Greet
Neq	Toward
Niykachiy	Send to speak to
Nuna	Soul
Ña	Already, now
Ñakapayay	Curse *(v.)*
Ñak'arichiy	Torture
Ñakay	Hardly
Ñañi	Tranquillity
Ñausa	Blind
Ñausay	Close the eyes
Ñawi	Eye
Ñawinlla	Pupil
Ñeqwin	Spinal cord
Ñiy	Relate, tell a story

Ñuñu	Breast, udder
Ñuñukuy	Suckle
Onqo	Sickness
Onqochiy	Be sick
Oqllay	Hatch
Oqocho	Chubby
Oqya	Gargle (n.)
Pacha	World
Pacha	Same
Pacha	Since (prep.)
Pachamama	Mother earth
Pachamit'a	Season of the year
Pakalla	On the sly
Pantay	Err
Para	Rain (n.)
Paray	Rain (v.)
Pauqarwariy	Spring (season)
Paytu	Lewd woman
Perqa	Wall
Perqalla	Cache-sexe
Pichuski	Ankle
Piki	Flea
Pillpa	Butterfly, vulva
Pisipay	Weaken, faint
Poqo	Ripe, mature
Puhllay	Play
Pukutay	Fog, mist
Puñunayay	Go to sleep
Puñupakay	Sleep in someone else's house
Puñupayay	Stay awake
Puriy	Go
P'aqla	Bald
P'anpa	Burial

P'anpay	Bury
P'anra	Potbellied
Pasña	Girl
P'enqachiy	Blush
P'osqo	Bitter
P'unchau	Day
P'unpu	Conceit
P'uru	Bladder
Phallallallay	Trill, warble
Phallay	Give birth
Phapa	Hoof
Pharararay	Flutter wings
Phosoqo	Foam
Phuchu	Sick
Phuruchay	Put on feathers
Phuyuchakuy	Cloud over
Phuyumay	Be cloudy
Phuyumayay	Threaten to cloud over
Phuyu phuyu	Thick clouds
Phuyuray	Uncloud, clear up
Phuyurqoy	Cloud over unexpectedly
Qala	Naked
Qallu	Tongue
Qañañaña	Howl of pain
Qapar	Taste *(n.)*
Qaqa	Cliff
Qaqapay	Hurl over a cliff
Qaqya	Belch *(n.)*
Qara	Bald, hairless
Qaracha	Mange
Qarapati	Scurf, dandruff
Qatipa	Spoor
Qayri	Male cousin
Q'ewi	Bend, curve

Qonqay	Forget
Qosa	Husband
Qoya	Wife
Qhachun	Sister-in-law
Qhale	Healthy
Qhaliyachiy	Heal
Qhamamamaq	Convalescent *(n.)*
Qhanpu	Tarantula
Qhaqyayoq	Tuberculosis
Qharqa	Snore
Qhasu	Broken
Qheantupa	Dawn *(n.)*
Qhepa	Behind
Qhepamama	Stepmother
Qhepañaña	Woman's sister (same mother)
Qhepayaya	Stepfather
Qhotototoy	Growl *(n.)*
Qhotoy	Spit *(v.)*

Ranra	Rocky
Rapha	Flame
Raphapapay	Blaze *(v.)*
Raqrapu	Greedy
Ratakuy	Grow fond of someone
Raurachiy	Kindle
Rikumuy	Visit
Rikuy	See
Rimariy	Stutter, stammer
Rimay	Language, speech
Runaka	People
Ruru	Fruit

Sach'a	Shrub
Sach'a sach'a	Thicket
Salla	Lover, concubine

Sallallay	Have intercourse with
Sama	Breath
Sapa	Each
Saphsay	Grow old
Sasa	Difficult
Sawa	Wedding, marriage
Sawaq	House, hut
Saway	Marry
Sayaqsayaq	Verbena
Sayri	Tobacco
Siki	Buttocks
Sinp'a	Pigtail
Sinp'anay	Unbraid hair
Siphsi	Drizzle
Sipi	Death
Sipiy	Kill
Sirasira	Scorpion
Siriq	Supine
Sisi	Ant
Siwiy	Whistle *(v.)*
Such'u	Crippled
Sullk'a	Small
Sullu	Abortion, fetus
Sulluchiy	Abort
Sumaq	Beautiful
Sumay	Honor, fame
Supiy	Fart *(v.)*
Suri	Perfume *(n.)*
Surk'an	Lungs
Suti	Name *(n.)*
Sutiyay	Nickname *(v.)*
Suyt'u	Snout
Takachu	Mustache
Taki	Song

Takillpa	Heel
Takiy	Sing
Tanqay	Push
Tawachaki	Quadruped
Tawak'uchu	Square
Tinta	Moth
Tintaya	Caterpillar
Toqe	Chief
Toqo	Carob tree
Toqocho	Big reed, baritone
Toqoro	Big stalk, bass
Tuqo	Son-in-law
Tusuy	Dance (v.)
Tutuy	Float (v.)
T'ampachiy	Tousle
T'apa	Nest
T'ikannay	Deflower
T'oqoy	Perforate
T'uyuna	Paddle
Thasnuy	Quench fire with water
Thukuy	Hesitate
Thutay	Eat (of moths)
Uchu	Chili pepper
Uhu	Cough
Uhyay	Drink
Uma	Head
Umachay	Lead, command
Uña	Breeding, brood
Upa	Deaf
Upallay	Keep quiet
Urin	South

Urunqoy	Bee
Uspha	Ashes
Uywaqe	Tutor
Wachay	Give birth to
Wach'oq	Adultery
Wahchu	Orphan
Wakha	Crazy
Wakhayay	Go mad
Wallqa	Necklace
Walla	Mountain range
Waman	Falcon
Wamera	Girl 10 to 14 years old, one going through puberty
Wanp'u	Canoe
Wañu	Dead
Waqaymit'a	Autumn
Waqo	Jaw
Waqsa	Fang, tusk
Waqta	Ribs
Warak'a	Blowgun
Waralli	Penis shield
Warma	Adolescent
Warmintin	Spouse, husband or wife
Watan watan	Annually
Wayayay	Grieve
Wayllapata	Grove
Wayllu	Idyl
Wayt'ay	Swim
Wihsa	Stomach
Wilali	Milk
Willka	Grandson
Wiraqocha	Sir
Wirp'a	Lip

Y	(Infinitive ending)
Yacha	Thought
Yachachiq	Teacher
Yachachiy	Teach
Yimququyay	Orgasm
Yuyu	Respect

ACKNOWLEDGMENTS

Some of the following people will be surprised to learn that they helped to produce this book; most will know what I mean: Mr. and Mrs. T. O. Mann, Peter E. Quint, Glenda Garvey, M.D., R. A. Sokolov, M.D., Robert Paul, Sherry Ortner, Charlotte Curtis, Jacqueline Duhau, Bernard Lichnerowicz, Calvert Watkins, Lynn Nesbit, Erica Spellman, Ben Brower, Fran McCullough, Alice Rosengard, Dick Passmore, Jacques De Brun, Claude Lévi-Strauss, the Hon. Sam Ervin, Kenneth Bleeth and the research staffs of the New York Public Library, the Time, Inc. Library and the Bibliothèque Nationale, Paris.